MATHEMATICS RESEARCH DEVELOPMENT

MATHEMATICAL EXPERIMENTS PLANNING IN CONCRETE TECHNOLOGY

MATHEMATICS RESEARCH DEVELOPMENT

MATHEMATICS RESEARCH DEVELOPMENT

MATHEMATICAL EXPERIMENTS PLANNING IN CONCRETE TECHNOLOGY

L. DVORKIN,
O. DVORKIN
AND
Y. RIBAKOV

Nova Science Publishers, Inc.
New York

NOTICE TO THE READER

LIBRARY OF CONGRESS CATALOGING-IN-PUBLICATION DATA

Mathematical experiments planning in concrete technology / editors, L. Dvorkin, O. Dvorkin, Y. Ribakov.
   p. cm.
Includes index.
ISBN 978-1-62100-283-3 (softcover)
1. Concrete--Mathematical models. I. Dvorkin, L. I. (Leonid Iosifovich) II. Dvorkin, Oleg. III. Ribakov, Y.
TA439.M2976 2011
620.1'360151--dc23
                    2011034209

Published by Nova Science Publishers, Inc. ✛ *New York*

CONTENTS

Preface   vii

Introduction   1

Chapter 1   System Analysis as a Modern Methodology for Solving Problems of Concrete Technology   3

Chapter 2   Methodological Fundamentals of Mathematical Experiment Planning   15

Chapter 3   The Main Tasks and Algorithms for Concrete Compositions Design   87

Chapter 4   Examples of Concrete Compositions Design Using Mathematical Modelling   111

Appendix   147

References   167

Index   169

ANNOTATION

Mathematical planning methods of experiments for the decision of tasks of concrete compositions design with the set of given properties are presented in a book. The procedures of obtaining of different types of mathematical models and their technological analysis are resulted. Examples of application of the mathematical planning methods of experiments and decision of the basic types of concrete technology tasks are considered as well.

The book can be used by civil engineers, specialists in concrete technology, research workers and students of Universities.

PREFACE

Optimal mixtures compositions design for concrete with specified properties is an important technological problem. Reliable performance of structures and economical parameters of their manufacturing depend to a considerable degree on the successful solving of it.

For concrete proportioning there is required a series of numerical dependences which take into consideration variety of factors affecting concrete properties. In spite of significant progress of concrete science it is still impossible to obtain acceptably accurate numerical dependences of concrete properties formed as a result of complicated physical-chemical processes. Because of that mathematical-statistical approach to obtaining multiple-factor dependencies of concrete properties is considered to be perspective one. One of the most effective methods of obtaining of such dependencies is based on application of methodology of experiments' mathematical planning.

In this book the authors made an attempt to give acceptable elemental conceptions and methodological principles of mathematical planning of experiments (MPE) related to problems of concrete technology and oriented on practitioners – civil and production engineers. There are given the examples of mathematical-statistical models of concrete properties obtaining by MPE using and application of the models in proportioning of concrete with specified properties.

The examples are developed on the bases of the authors researches carried out in National University of Water Management and Nature Resources Use (Ukraine) and Ariel University Center of Samaria (Israel).

The authors are thankful to the colleagues for their help in the experimental and analytical studies and hope that book will be interesting and useful for the wide range of experts.

Also, authors will be thankful for all the comments and remarks of the readers.

INTRODUCTION

Production of concrete and structural elements with required characteristics and durability is related to many problems arising at design of concrete mixtures compositions. Methodology of solving such problems involves simultaneous consideration of many factors (compositions of initial components, their contents, compacting and forming of mixes, hardening regimes, etc.) and providing many parameters (workability, strength, frost resistance, water impermeability, etc.). It is difficult to consider the influence of above-mentioned factors using traditional methods of experimentation due to high work complexity. Using a system approach and mathematical methods for solving such problems significantly reduces the experimental efforts. Additionally, applying computers increases the efficiency of concrete mixtures design.

Conducting experiments to study the influence of certain factors on the concrete properties using mathematical methods of planning enables getting the result in a form of equation (mathematical models) that adequately describes the real dependencies with a reasonable statistically based probability. The equations enable solving the problem of providing required concrete properties, concrete composition and technology optimization, both within and out the frame of the experiment. Using mathematical models allows performing effective technical and economic analysis of adopted technological solutions and optimization of economic parameters.

The book includes four chapters. The first chapter deals with general principles of system analysis application for solving problems of concrete technology. It explains the main terms and rules of system approach, mathematical modeling of concrete compositions with required properties.

The second chapter describes the methodology of mathematical experiments' planning. The main types of problems, solved by using mathematical planning, are analysed, and the optimization criteria for solving concrete technology problems are formulated. Methods for obtaining linear and quadratic models are presented. Issues of statistical analysis of regression equations are also considered. Examples of applying the above-mentioned methodology to solve typical problems are given.

In the third chapter, the main tasks and algorithms are described, and the fourth one presents examples for solving problems, related to design of concrete compositions using mathematical experiment planning. Real data from research carried out by the authors are used.

The authors are thankful to the colleagues for the help in the experimental and analytical studies, results of which are given in the book.

Chapter 1

SYSTEM ANALYSIS AS A MODERN METHODOLOGY FOR SOLVING PROBLEMS OF CONCRETE TECHNOLOGY

1.1. ESSENCE OF SYSTEM APPROACH TO SOLVING CONCRETE TECHNOLOGY PROBLEMS

Modern scientific and technological revolution requires radical increase in efficiency of manufacturing processes and management by using all possible reserves, implementing the most advanced technology and technique, automation of manufacturing and control processes, wide usage of mathematical methods, computing and cybernetic machines. These conditions, as well as the continuous increase in production scale and complicated relationships among different factors, processes and phenomena, lead to strong requirements concerning the methodology of scientific and technological analysis for solving actual problems.

In recent years, system analysis, including a comprehensive feasibility pre-investigation, comparison of alternatives and selection of optimal solutions, based on extensive application of mathematical modeling and computers applications, is widely applied. The basic premise of system analysis is getting a set of relationships between phenomena and processes in a form of controlled cybernetic systems.

Depending on the research and management goals, the system can be limited by a certain scale and split into subsystems. For example, production of concrete and reinforced concrete elements can be represented as a complex stochastic system, including the following subsystems: design of concrete composition, production of concrete mixture and reinforcing details, casting and hardening. Each system is a subsystem of a more common system. Production of structural elements is a subsystem within a more complicated system of construction works. Consequently, design of concrete composition can be represented as a system and split into two subsystems—the initial components choice and defining relations between them.

The essence of a system approach to solving the problem comes to each subsystem that should function optimally within the total system and according to its purpose. This problem of system managing is to formulate goals, identifying characteristics and system parameters affecting achievement of the goal, indicators and criteria of effective activity as well as obtaining a mathematical model and developing on its basis algorithms and programs in order to determine the optimal values of factors.

After studying the qualitative process structure, identifying and excluding factors that have negligible effect on the efficiency criteria and performance indexes, and setting limits and regulated factors, the system analysis allows mathematical modeling, enabling expressing quantitatively the character and impact of individual elements and their interactions. To solve technological problems, it is necessary to use deterministic and probabilistic mathematical models. Deterministic models are the result of physical and chemical processes investigation. In the technology of building materials and structural elements, production deterministic models describe only the simplest regularities. Developing a theory for complex composite materials like concrete requires clarification and mathematical description of processes undergoing in complex systems. Despite significant progress in concrete science and development of theoretical concepts that describe many aspects of the concrete structure and its relationship with physical and mechanical properties, the theory of concrete is still not perfect and requires further improvement. Concrete is a complicated research object due to the complexity of its hardening processes, deformation and fracture, heterogeneous and multi-component structure that is unstable in time, continuous interaction with environment, etc.

Concrete and other composite building materials as well as technological processes for their production belong to badly organized or so-called diffusive systems. For such systems, many diverse factors should be taken into account. For diffuse systems, the knowledge about the mechanism of all phenomena occurring in them is limited. In this case, statistical and cybernetic methods are the most effective. The first allows developing recommendations for optimal behavior of the system taking into account uncertainties and to present the experimental data in a standardized form in order to perform the concentration of information to analytical expression (regression equation). It is especially important in modern research, when the amount of information is rapidly growing and it is required to present it in the most compact and complete form. The second method reveals, first of all, the functional dependence of the system on the environment, abstracting from the internal cause-effect relationships, i.e., using known "black box" principles. Cybernetic modeling is characterized by inherent unity of the functional approach and optimization as a means of obtaining data for the best system management.

The task of mathematical modeling is to obtain some idea about the response surface factors, which can be analytically represented in a form of the following function:

$$M_{\{y\}} = \varphi\left(X_1, X_2, X_3, ..., X_n\right), \qquad (1.1)$$

where y is the optimization parameter, i.e., the investigated parameter of the system, X_i – variable factors of the system.

The most convenient form to represent the unknown response function is the polynomial:

$$Y = \beta_0 + \sum_{i=1}^{n} \beta_i X_i + \sum_{i=1}^{n} \beta_{ii} X_i^2 + \sum_{i \neq j} \beta_{ij} X_i X_j + ... \qquad (1.2)$$

The form and the exponent of the polynomial are preliminary chosen using theoretical analysis and then adjusted statistically. Estimation of polynomial models regression coefficients β can be found based on the experimental results. According to the modern mathematical theory of experiment, the most successful combination of cybernetic and statistical approaches for investigation of complex diffuse systems is used in methods of mathematical experiment planning, which is currently well developed and used in different branches of science and technology, including technology of concrete.

An active multi-factorial experiment has several essential advantages over the single- factorial one. Optimal organization of the investigation yields a reduction in the experimental work amount by two to ten times (depending on the number of factors) and increases the reliability of the results, taking into account the factor's interaction. When planning the experiment, mathematical methods play an active role in all stages of research: formalizing the preliminary available information before carrying out the experiments, during testing, data processing and decision-making.

Possible abstraction of complex causal relationships at the stage of obtaining diffusive systems' mathematical models can significantly reveal these relationships and then further analysis models and gain insight into the processes occurring in the system. This is the cognitive value of mathematical models that are not only necessary for rapid, automatic control of the system but are also a source of its deeper understanding and theory development.

The most important goal of mathematical modeling is optimization of technological process characteristics. There are two groups of optimization problems:

a) selection of the most suitable technological regime (composition) - technology optimizaton;
b) keeping a given (in some cases the most suitable) regime.

These problems can be solved separately and simultaneously.

In a common case, the problem of finding the optimal state of the system can be formulated as follows: required to identify positive values of technological factors $x_1 \geq 0$, $x_2 \geq 0...x_n \geq 0$, satisfying the system of inequalities (constraints):

$$\left. \begin{array}{l} P_1 = f_1(x_1, x_2, x_3, ..., x_n) \leq \alpha_1 (\text{or} > \alpha_1) \\ P_2 = f_2(x_1, x_2, x_3, ..., x_n) \leq \alpha_2 (\text{or} > \alpha_2) \\ P_3 = f_3(x_1, x_2, x_3, ..., x_n) \leq \alpha_3 (\text{or} > \alpha_3) \\ \cdots \cdots \cdots \cdots \cdots \cdots \cdots \cdots \cdots \cdots \cdots \cdots \\ \cdots \cdots \cdots \cdots \cdots \cdots \cdots \cdots \cdots \cdots \cdots \cdots \\ P_n = f_n(x_1, x_2, x_3, ..., x_n) \leq \alpha_n (\text{or} > \alpha_n) \end{array} \right\} \qquad (1.3)$$

So that

$$P_\kappa = f_k(x_1, x_2, x_3 ... x_n) = \min(\max) \qquad (1.4)$$

where $P_1, P_2, ..., P_n$ – effectiveness parameters; P_κ – effectiveness criterion or aim function.

For solving technological problems, it is possible to use mate-mathematical models that differ by:

a) number of inequalities in the system (constraints);
b) the functions' nature;
c) number of factors;
d) the nature of relationships between the factors;
e) the intensity degree and nature of the factor's variation over time.

For each group of models, it is necessary to use specially developed mathematical methods for finding the optimal solution. The function's extremum can be found by solving a system of algebraic equations that has the following form:

$$\frac{\partial F(x_1, x_2, x_3 \ldots x_n)}{\partial x_j}, \qquad j = 1, 2, 3 \ldots n \cdot \qquad (1.5)$$

As the number of variables and constraints on their solution for such a system increases, the computational effort also increases. In this regard, along with analytical methods, numerical optimization methods, realized using modern software and computer technologies, have practical interest.

1.2. CYBERNETIC METHOD FOR PREDICTING CONCRETE PROPERTIES

The quality of concrete is determined by combination of its constructional and technological properties. The quality may be achieved using a system of reliable research-based methods for prediction of concrete properties. There are experimental and design methods for prediction of concrete properties.

Experimental methods for obtaining concrete characteristics are used during its manufacture or after the material's production. To realize the concrete quality-control problems, experimental and design express-methods for estimation of concrete mix properties and mechanical characteristics of concrete after hardening have the highest importance. The main advantage of analytical methods is that they allow prediction of concrete properties already at the design stage, considering possible changes in quality of final product by changing the properties of initial materials and parameters of technological regimes. It improves the production efficiency by saving material and labor resources and enhances the role of scientific basis of technology. Development of analytical methods for prediction of concrete properties becomes particularly important as computer-based automated manufacturing control systems are more and more used in practice. These methods require strict quantitative relations allowing getting the optimal solution for a complicated multi-factorial system.

Development of scientific principles for prediction of concrete properties is one of the central problems throughout the history of concrete, its investigation and development. Solution of this problem brought the scientists in the end of the last century to two approaches: structural and factorial. According to the first approach, the indexes of concrete properties directly depend on the parameters of its structure (density, porosity, etc.). Following the second approach, the indexes depend on the most important technological factors like water-cement ratio, water content, etc. In practice, the second approach is more useful due to relatively easy measurement of technological factors, possibility of moving directly from the properties prediction to design of concrete mixture composition.

As experimental and theoretical data in the concrete technology are accumulated, it clearly shows the necessity of taking into account a large number of factors that affect the concrete properties. It is caused by the desire improvement of the prediction accuracy and also to get pretty full mathematical models of concrete properties that could be used in solving problems of efficiency analysis and technological processes control. Traditional technological dependences, including maximum two or three variables, do not enable overcoming the "factor barrier" in predicting the properties of concrete.

The first analytical dependences, proposed by Fere in 1982, were based on relations between the concrete properties and its structure. These relations enable, to some extent, overcoming the factor barrier. There are several directions in theoretical studies focused on relations between structure and properties of concrete. They are based on solid-state physics, physical-chemical mechanics of disperse systems, atomic-molecular theory and theory of artificial conglomerates. Each of them is very fruitful. For example, development of the main rheology provisions enabled to describe the structural and mechanical properties of concrete mixtures. Considering concrete as an elastic-viscous material enabled to propose structural models and hypotheses of deformation and destruction mechanism as well as to find expressions for relevant concrete characteristics. Principles of physical and chemical mechanics of disperse systems created a basis for controlled structure forming theories as well as many theoretical design equations. Theory of artificial conglomerates reveals a way for producing concrete with optimal structure and allows effective prediction of its properties.

Understanding concrete as a capillary-porous composite material forms a basis for studying the influence of concrete structure on its properties. It became the source for development of known and finding new emerging theories of concrete structure. Studying the porous space and its relationship with strength, frost resistance, permeability, etc., as well as investigating the complex of features related to the physical mechanism of concrete properties synthesis are the most realistic and promising ways to create a system of design analytical relations in concrete technology.

Concrete structure formation and synthesis of its properties is a complex of very complicated processes, occurring in concrete from atomic-molecular level to macrostructure. Despite the fact that the problem is central to the modern concrete theory, some assumptions and approximations that are acceptable for technological reasons yield errors in calculations. Structural prediction method of some concrete properties is unacceptable at the moment, due to the influence of a large number of different factors on concrete composition and production regimes. In these conditions, application of cybernetic methods for prediction and management of concrete properties is effective when the set of controlled factors and the range for their possible changes are concretized.

Cybernetics can be viewed as science for managing complex systems. Concrete technology and production of reinforced concrete elements belongs to such systems. The task of this system is to ensure optimum quality of materials and products "output" by adjusting the "input" factors.

Cybernetic method is a modern modification of the factorial approach for obtaining quantitative relations, required in order to solve problems of prediction and control of concrete properties. The main—and practically the most—valuable in the cybernetic approach is the possibility of predicting the behavior of the controlled object, abstracting in a certain measure from its material, energy and structural characteristics, i.e., on the basis of functional similarity. The available information, obtained by the cybernetic investigation of concrete and due to the previous research, can usually move from principles of "black" to "gray" box, when the researchers already have some preliminary data that has mainly a qualitative nature. The task is reduced to obtaining an adequate mathematical description of the investigated dependencies for stationary or stationary and non-stationary conditions.

Mathematical models are cybernetic tools that reveal the external functional dependences of the system without analysis of internal causal relations. However, the possibility of obtaining specific information about the behavior of the system greatly contributes to theoretical research.

Wide implementation of computers and mathematical methods in science and practice promoted in recent decades the rapid development of research in various fields of technology, including concrete technology. As a result, numerous mathematical models were developed, and important practical conclusions were obtained.

Accumulated to date considerable experience in applying mathematical modeling in concrete technology shows its effectiveness, mainly in the complex optimization tasks, where using other methods is impossible or is more time and labor consuming.

In cybernetic approach, mathematical models are obtained, formalizing the statistical information about the system behavior by varying some technological factors. Obtaining such information is possible on the basis of "passive" and "active" experiments. In the "active" experiment, carried out using mathematical planning methods, it is possible to obtain models with a minimum amount of work according to the preliminary conditions for the regression analysis. While planning an experiment, an active role is paid to the mathematical methods at all stages of the research: the formalization of preliminary information available before performing the experiments, during the experiments, results processing and decision making.

Polynomial factor models, as opposed to the structural ones, enable estimating the influence of the factors that were taken into account and obtaining quantitative performance of their interaction. However, getting models in strictly defined conditions is not a sufficient condition for the cybernetic method. Obtaining the models can be regarded as the first stage. An important additional condition is periodic adaptation of models, i.e., their adjustments based on current information. Application of adapted models is particularly appropriate in solving problems of prediction and control of concrete properties in production conditions when the uncontrolled input indignations are present. Cybernetic method with feedback and adjustment of mathematical models is promising and began to find practical application in concrete technology.

Multifactor prediction of concrete properties has the most practical significance when it is aimed at selecting an effective combination of technological factors for achieving the required quality parameters of concrete.

System analysis is used to solve complex problems (mainly semi-structured problems with mixed quantitative and qualitative estimation) by studying the properties of systems and interaction between goals and means of achieving them. Such problems include achievement of optimal concrete properties. It includes selecting the desired technical characteristics of concrete mixture, strength of cement, quality parameters of sand and crushed stone (gravel), type of admixtures, selecting the regime parameters, calculating the contents of initial components per 1 m^3 of concrete mixture. All these factors are aimed at getting concrete that corresponds to the structural design requirements in a most effective way and at a minimum cost. They can be regarded as subsystems providing the optimal concrete properties. The last one can be represented as a subsystem of more general systems for design of concrete and reinforced concrete elements and their production technology. System analysis develops the traditional methods of scientific analysis. It is effective in solving various problems in presence of uncertainty and infinite number of possible alternatives. Uncertainties in management of concrete properties are caused by its complexity as a study object. It is because limited knowledge about concrete hardening, its deformation and destruction, heterogeneous and multi-component nature of its structure that is unstable in time and is in continuous interaction with the environment. It can be shown by simple calculations that the design technology of reinforced concrete structures, even at very simplified scheme of estimation of only three choices at each of 14 stages, yields 3^{14}, or 4,782,969 possible solutions. Similarly, it is easy to prove that for problems related to providing design concrete properties an infinite number of alternatives are practically possible.

Any object of the system is characterized by input, output, performance processes, feedback and limitations. An "input" to concrete as a system is a combination of following factors: technological, determined by the external environment; economic, etc. The "output" includes a set of properties and economic parameters that determine the effectiveness of concrete in structural design. A system creating the concrete structure is a set of processes resulting in transforming the input factors in the output parameters. Using the feedback, information about the concrete properties and its performance returns to the input, allowing adjustment of the contributing factors. To evaluate the functional characteristics of the system, it is required to construct mathematical models that adequately reflect the relationships between individual elements of the research object. Influence of technological factors in models of concrete properties can be considered directly in the polynomial equations and indirectly in integral criteria in the criteria equations.

The probabilistic mathematical models are obtained using the regression analysis of traditional ("passive") or active experiment. An algorithm of an active experiment is implemented using the mathematical experiments' planning methods, which were recently well developed and can be applied for experimental works in various fields of science and technology, including the technology of concrete and reinforced concrete. The methods of mathematical experiment planning are the closest to the system approach from the initial conditions viewpoint. They investigate the studied object, taking into account the possible factors interaction, enabling obtaining a model that adequately discloses the direct and backward links in the system.

1.3. System Analysis at a Stage of Providing Optimal Concrete Properties

The general scheme of system analysis in the concrete technology at the first stage includes determining the optimal compositions of concrete mixtures and providing the complete complex of given concrete properties. During the next stages, the initial components and technological process conditions are optimized, and, if it is necessary, the design parameters of concrete compositions are adjusted.

For each problem, optimality criteria and constraints are formulated. As the system analysis problems become deeper, the optimality criteria are also more complicated. For providing optimum concrete properties, the simplest optimality criterion is the minimum cement consumption. The most complex optimality criterion is the minimum cost of a concrete element "in work" per unit, i.e., the total costs, including the cost of its production, transportation, installation and repairing during the lifetime.

The minimum cost criterion in problems of choosing the best technology solutions in real conditions may be used taking into account the limitations of available resources (cement, fuel, labor, etc.) as well as the required performance level. Approved decisions are often at the same compromise. Due to limited number of alternatives, considered in effectiveness analysis, related to the choice of cement, admixtures and aggregates, conditions and hardening duration, mixture workability, the minimum cost and rational cement and fuel use criteria are simplified. In this case, the optimization problem solution is aimed at searching the only option leading to the extreme (minimum) criterion value.

The main technical parameters for selecting the cement type are its chemical-mineralogical and material components composition, ultimate strength, strength after certain hardening time, including if necessary the heat treatment; cement paste consistency and fineness; a number of other parameters, defined by concrete design requirements, conditions of its lifetime in elements and structures.

For assessing the cement use efficiency relative parameters, describing the cement content or its cost per strength unit, as well as the ratio between the concrete strength and cement content, were proposed. However, these parameters are convenient for comparing efficiency of various cements just for concrete with identical strength values, obtained under certain concrete-hardening conditions.

A more universal parameter is the coefficient of rational cement use $K_{r.c.u}$. It represents the ratio between specific cost of cement for producing concrete mix or reinforced concrete (RC) elements with given properties at some standard version, to cement cost and methods that yield a decrease of cement content for given technological solution:

$$K_{r.c.u} = \frac{S_{c.st}}{S_c + S_{t.m}} = \frac{Ct_{c.st}Ct_{st}}{Ct_c C + S_{t.m}} \qquad (1.6)$$

where $S_{c.st}$ and S_c are specific cost of cement spent on 1 m^3 of concrete or a certain RC element at standard and given versions of the technological solution, respectively; $S_{t.m}$ are the specific resulted expenses for a complex of technological methods aimed at reduction of cement content without concrete deterioration (adding admixtures, electric heating or steaming the concrete mix, etc.); $Ct_{c.st}$ and Ct_c are expences of standard and applied cements, respectively; C_{st} and C are the costs of standard and applied cements for producing concrete with design requirements, respectively.

The cost criterion $K_{r.c.u}$ at identical cost of standard and compared cements becomes a physical one. It represents the relative cement content, expressed, for example, by the ratio of cement content, required for producing concrete with certain quality at normal hardening conditions, to that at heat treatment.

$K_{r.c.u}$ enables estimating the efficiency of cement use in analysis of technological and design solutions, related to decrease the materials expense of concrete and RC elements. For example, for comparative assessment of concrete strength in structures, it is convenient to use the following expression:

$$K'_{r.c.u} = \frac{S_c^0 V}{(S'_c + S_{a.e})V'} \qquad (1.7)$$

where S_c^0, S_c' are the cement costs per 1 m³ of standard and compared concretes, respectively; V and V' are the volumes of the standard and compared structural elements, respectively; $S_{a.e}$ are additional expenses, related to the changes in concrete strength in RC elements.

For consumers of concrete with admixtures, the price level acceptability results from the following condition:

$$\Delta S_{cnc} = K_e C_{s.r}, \qquad (K_e > 1) \qquad\qquad (1.8)$$

where ΔS_{cn} is the difference between costs of concrete with and without admixture; K_e is a coefficient, denoting the price efficiency of concrete with admixture, $C_{s.r}$ - cost of saved resources.

Qualitative advantages of concrete with admixtures in specific concrete application conditions can be used with various aims. Increase of concrete strength may be used for varying the elements' section, reducing the required reinforcement, decreasing the construction duration, etc.

Chapter 2

METHODOLOGICAL FUNDAMENTALS OF MATHEMATICAL EXPERIMENT PLANNING

2.1. GENERAL INFORMATION: PRELIMINARY OBJECT INVESTIGATION

Mathematical planning of experiment (MPE) means carrying out tests according to a scheme that was developed in advance. Such a scheme is characterized by optimal amount of experimental work and statistical requirements. The experiment-planning theory is based on probabilistic-statistical methods, allowing reasonable determination of minimum number and composition of experiments, as well as their order that is required to get quantitative relations between the investigated parameter and factors that affect it.

Obtaining a mathematical model of the investigated object is the basic task of MPE. The task of obtaining a mathematical model is to find a relationship that characterizes the dependence between the optimization parameter η and independent variables.

In the most general form,

$$\eta = \varphi\ (x_1, x_2,\ldots,x_k), \tag{2.1}$$

where $x_1, x_2,\ldots,x_k$ are independent variables (factors) that may be varied during the experiments.

If MPE is used, the parameter η (response function) is approximised in a polynomial form:

$$\eta = \beta_0 + \sum_{i}^{k} \beta_i \, x_i + \sum_{i<j}^{k} \beta_{ij} \, x_i \, x_j + \sum_{i}^{k} \beta_{ii} \, x_i^2 + ..., \qquad (2.2)$$

where β_0, β_i, β_{ij}, β_{ii} are theoretical regression coefficients.

The regression coefficients b_0, b_i, b_{ij}, b_{ii}, are determined from the experiments. These coefficients estimate the theoretical ones. Then Eq. (2.2) takes the form:

$$\hat{y} = b_0 + \sum_{i}^{k} b_i \, x_i + \sum_{i<j}^{k} b_{ij} \, x_i \, x_j + \sum_{i}^{k} b_{ii} \, x_i^2 + ..., \qquad (2.3)$$

where $\hat{y}$ is the design value of the optimization parameter.

The regression coefficients values enable to estimate the influence of relevant factors. Eq. (2.3) can be interpreted as some surface in k-dimensional space (Figure 2.1).

Successful use of MPE depends primarily on the correct problem statement. Thus, the experimenter should be able to clearly identify the information volume and content to be obtained from experiments, as well as the appropriateness and applicability of MPE for specific conditions.

When defining the simplest task or at the first stage of the investigation, it is often desired to get first order regression equations or incomplete quadratic equations. Solving most optimization problems is associated, usually, with using second-order polynomials. Third-order polynomial dependences, usually, are not used for solving problems of concrete technology.

Planning an experiment is conducted in several stages. First, a preliminary study of the investigated object is studied. Then, an appropriate mathematical model is obtained and interpreted. Finally, if necessary, the results are technically implemented.

Preliminary study of the investigated object includes: setting objectives, collecting and processing the a priori information, developing a working hypothesis, choice of optimization parameters, independent variables and constraints, carrying out a preliminary experiment.

Optimization criteria for optimization problems should be clearly defined. In practice various simple and complex, technical, economic and technical-economic optimization criteria are used (Table 2.1). Optimization criteria used in technological problems can go to some absolute or conditional extremum, and in multi-criteria problems, they are found in a compromise region.

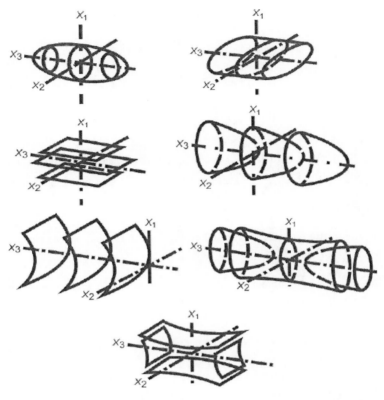

Figure 2.1. Three-dimensional surfaces characterizing stationary region, described by a second order equations for $k = 3$.

The quest for extreme values of the optimization criterion is typical especially for problems when the criterion is presented by a ratio, for example, the concrete properties to its cost or to the cost of cement or energetic resource. Figure 2.2 demonstrates the dependence of the efficiency coefficient (k_e) that is the ratio of concrete strength (R_{cmp}) to the specific cement content (C) on the parameter that determines the density and takes into account the degree of cement hydration (α) and water-cement ratio (W/C).

Typical concrete composition optimization problems allow achieving conditional extremum, i.e., maximum (minimum) possible criterion value under given constraints (e.g., minimum possible volume of cement stone concentration for given values of concrete strength, mix workability, etc.).

Table 2.1. Main optimization criteria for design of concrete compositions

Resource expenditure (per 1 m^3 of concrete mix, element, structure): $X \rightarrow \min.$
Relation between the resource expenditure to the concrete property parameter (P_i): $X/P_i \rightarrow \min.$
Specific cost index *: $C \rightarrow \min,$ where C is the cost of 1 m^3 of concrete, element, structure; resources cost; equivalent cost, etc.
The ratio of specific cost parameters for the given (C) and reference concretes (C_0)*: $C/C_o \rightarrow \min.$
The ratio between specific cost and properties parameters (or vice versa)*: $C/P_i \rightarrow \min$ (or $P_i/C \rightarrow \max$).
The ratio between parameters of concrete properties (P_i) and expenditure of material or energy resources required for its production (X): $P_i/X \rightarrow \max,$ where X is the expenditure of cement, aggregates, admixtures, heat, electricity, etc.
The ratio between properties parameters for the given concrete (P_i) and those of the reference one (P_o): $P_i/P_o \rightarrow \max (\min).$
Properties parameter of (complex, correlation properties) for concrete mix or concrete (P_i): $P_i \rightarrow \max (\min),$ were P_i is concrete mix workability; strength, frost resistance, shrinkage of concrete, etc.

Note: * The optimization criterion is considered just when the design properties of concrete are mandatory provided.

If an optimal composition of concrete and its structure are defined by two or more optimality criteria, they are in a compromise region. From Figure 2.3, for example, follows that for the compressive strength of the investigated concrete $R_{cmp} \geq 40$ MPa and its frost resistance (number of freezing and thawing cycles), $F \geq 400$ is provided by entrained air content $V_{air} = 2,7\%$. Higher values of V_{air} yield an increase of F, but decreases R_{cmp}.

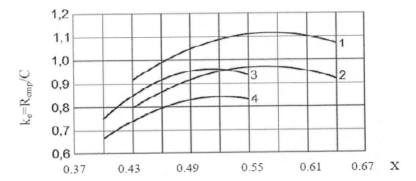

Figure 2.2. Dependence between efficiency coefficient (k_e) for different cement's ultimate compressive strengths (R_{cem}) and concrete density, $X = \dfrac{0{,}647\alpha}{0{,}319\alpha + W/C}$

where α – cement hydration degree; W/C – water – cement ratio: 1 – R_{cem} = 50 MPa (Vebe time = 11...20 sec.); 2 – R_{cem} = 50 MPa (Slump = 1...4 cm); 3 – R_{cem} = 40 MPa (Vebe time = 11...20 sec.); 4 – R_{cem} = 50 MPa (Slump = 1...4 cm).

When defining the optimization tasks, it is necessary to consider the relationship between different optimization criteria. When the concrete properties' parameters are used as optimization criteria, the relationships between them are caused by interaction of corresponding structural parameters, determining the considered properties. Coincidence in vectors of properties changes and their optimum values is possible when a change of corresponding structural parameters is proportional. For example, the ratio between the density of cement stone in concrete (X) and the volume concentration of cement stone ($V_{c.s}$) is some function of cement content (C) and W/C:

$$X\!\!\left/\!\!V_{c.s} \right. = f(C, W/C) \cdot$$

Optimization criteria, presented as relationships between properties values and resources specific expenditure or cost (Table 2.1), are more general than corresponding criteria, characterizing the direct resources expenditure. Their form can be easily modified to that of the last at necessary constraints in corresponding calculation expressions.

At the stage of preliminary object study for formalization of a priori information, in some cases, it is useful to carry out a psychological experiment aimed at objective processing of data obtained from experts surveys or review of studies published in the literature. It allows a more correct formulation of research problems, reducing the amount of further experimental work and enables adopting or rejecting some preliminary hypotheses.

In most cases, a psychological experiment is conducted to compare influence of various factors on the optimization parameters. It allows correct selection of factors for the next active experiment and proper exclusion of other factors from further consideration. In such way, the factors, their variation intervals and main level can be selected.

When solving such problems, it is possible to use a priori ranking of factors based on rank correlation methods. A priori ranking of factors is based on the fact that the factors that according to a priori information can have a significant impact are ranked in descending order of their contributions. The contribution of each factor is measured according to its rank in a set of all factors (prepared by the researcher or a specialist in the survey, the article author, etc.), taking into account intended impact of each factor on the optimization parameters. The poll results (or ranking according to the data available in the literature) are treated as follows. First the sum of ranks for the all factors, $\sum_{j=1}^{m} a_{ij}$, is determined, and then the difference between the sum of ranks for each factor and the average sum of ranks is obtained:

$$\Delta^3 = \sum_{l=1}^{m} a_{ij} - \frac{\sum_{i=1}^{k}\sum_{j=1}^{m} a_{ij}}{k} = \sum_{j=1}^{m} a_{ij} - T \qquad (2.4)$$

where α_{ij} is the rank of each factor i for researcher j, m is the number of researchers and k is the number of factors. These data enables obtaining an average a priori ranks diagram, satisfying the preliminary condition of researchers opinion consistency degree using concordation coefficient (W):

$$W = \frac{S}{\frac{1}{12}m^2(k^3 - k) - m\sum_{j=1}^{m} T_i} \qquad (2.5)$$

where S is a sum of square deviations ($\sum_{j=1}^{m}\Delta i^2$),

$$T_i = \frac{1}{12} \sum_{t_j} \left(t_j^3 - t_j \right)$$

(2.6)

t_j is a number of equal ranks in ranking number j.

Example 2.1. It is required to choose the factors affecting the concrete strength in terms of heat-moisture treatment under the following constraints: the portland cement should be produced by one plant; quartz sand and crushed granite stone have unchanged characteristics; the production technology, storage and testing of concrete specimens are constant.

Based on a priori information, 15 factors that have a certain influence on concrete strength were initially selected. For ranking the factors, experts questioning formalization method was used. A questionnaire for these factors and their proposed boundary changes are shown in Table 2.2.

The experts should place the factors in descending order of their influence on concrete strength. The ranks matrix after the poll was brought to a form so that the total ranks sum for each researcher was $\frac{k(k+1)}{2}$.

According to the survey results (Table 2.2), the ranks sum $\sum\limits_{j=1}^{m} a_{ij}$ for each factor i was obtained. Here, j is the researcher's number and m is the total number of researchers participated in the survey. After that, an average sum of ranks T_r was obtained for k factors and deviations Δ_i between the sum of ranks for each factor and the average sum of ranks was found. The researchers' opinion consistency degree was assessed by concordation coefficient and subsequent statistical assessment of its significance according to χ^2 - distribution. The concordation coefficient $W = 0.654$. It enables accepting the hypothesis of coordination between the researchers with probability of more than 99% and to prepare based on the survey an average a priory diagram for impact ranks of the considered factors on the concrete strength at selected limits of changes (Figure 2.4).

Analysis of the ranks diagram shows that the factors distribution is close to exponential and not uniform. It definitely allows emphasizing of key factors, and some of others can be attributed to the so-called "noise field." These most significant factors affecting the strength of concrete, subjected to heat-moisture treatment, include: ultimate cement strength (R_{cem}), water-cement ratio (W/C), temperature of isothermal heating (T_{is}), duration of isothermal heating (τ_{is}) and temperature rise velocity (V_r). The weakest factor, according to the results of a questionnaire is the plate-like grains content ($m_{p.l}$) from 10 to 30%.

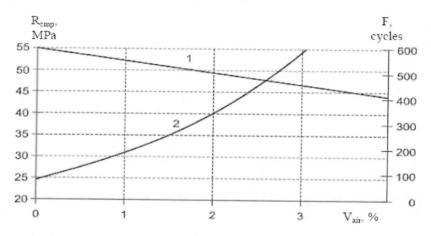

Figure 2.3. Dependence between concrete strength R_{cmp} (1), frost resistance F (2) and entrained air volume (V_{air}).

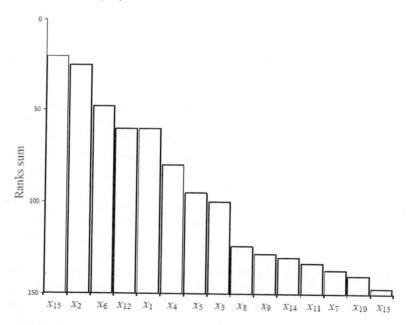

Figure 2.4. Diagram of a priory factors ranking x_i.

Table 2.2. A questionnaire for experts

No.	Factors affecting the concrete strength	Limits of factors changes	Expert No. 1	2	3	4	5	6	7	8	9	10	11	12	Sum of ranks	Deviation of ranks sum from the mean value Δi	Δi^2	Overall rank
x_1	Cement content (C) for W/C=const, kg/m³	250-400	6	4	3	4	4	8	6	6	7	5	4	5	62	-34	1156	5
x_2	Water-cement ratio (W/C)	0,5 – 0,7	3	4	1	2	3	1	2	4	1	2	2	2	27	-69	4761	2
x_3	Sand content in aggregates mix (r)	0,3 – 0,5	7	8	10	9	8	8	7	9	6	9	8	11	100	4	16	8
x_4	Temperature increase velocity (V_{inc}), degrees/hour	10 - 30	6	4	8	10	7	10	7	6	5	6	9	5	83	-13	169	6
x_5	Duration of exposure before steaming, (τ_{exp}), hours	1 - 5	8	10	6	7	6	8	7	8	11	9	8	7	95	-1	1	7
x_6	Isothermal heating temperature, $(T_{is})^0C$	70-100	4	5	2	3	5	3	4	7	5	4	4	3	49	-47	2209	3
x_7	Sand fineness modulus (M_{fn})	1,6 – 2,7	13	12	12	10	8	11	10	9	12	14	12	14	137	41	1681	13
x_8	Coarseness of crushed stone, (D_{max}) mm	10 - 40	8	10	11	12	10	9	10	9	11	12	10	12	124	28	784	9

Table 2.2. (Continued)

No.	Factors affecting the concrete strength	Limits of factors changes	Expert No.												Sum of ranks	Deviation of ranks sum from the mean value Δi	Δi^2	Overall rank
			1	2	3	4	5	6	7	8	9	10	11	12				
x_9	Cooling velocity, (V_{cl}), degrees/hour	10 - 30	10	11	12	11	13	12	13	10	10	8	10	11	131	35	1225	10
x_{10}	Mixing duration, (τ_{mx}) min.	1 - 3	13	12	13	13	12	11	12	11	10	11	12	12	142	46	2116	14
x_{11}	Strength of crushed stone, $(R_{c.s})$, MPa	100-170	12	11	9	12	13	10	11	11	8	12	13	11	133	37	1369	12
x_{12}	Isothermal heating duration, $(\tau_{i.s})$, hours	3 - 6	5	3	6	5	7	4	7	5	6	5	4	5	62	-34	1156	4
x_{13}	Plate-like grains content $(m_{p.l})$, %	10 -30	11	12	13	12	11	12	13	12	13	11	12	11	143	47	2209	15
x_{14}	Open sample surface degree, (S_o), %	0 - 50	12	11	13	9	12	11	10	11	12	11	10	10	132	36	1296	11
x_{15}	Ultimate cement strength, (R_{cem}), MPa	40-60	2	3	1	1	1	2	1	2	3	1	2	1	20	-76	5776	1

An important requirement for factors in the experiment's planning is that there is no correlation between them. It does not mean that between factors should not be any relation. It is necessary and sufficient that such relations are indirect. For example, in studies related to concrete mixes without plasticizers and constant materials, it is impossible to plan simultaneously the concrete slump and the water content, as if other conditions are equal, the water content is constant for a given concrete slump value.

When choosing the factors, their controllability degree and possibility of providing a given variation level should be considered. Planning of difficult-controlled factors should be done using special techniques. It is better if the factors are quantitatively assessed. However, it is possible to plan factors according to their qualitative indicators also.

For any value of the factors, the variation levels should provide an opportunity to carry out the experiment and measure the output parameter. For example, if the output parameter is the concrete mix slump, then the sand portion in the aggregates mix, the water content and the amount of admixtures should ensure obtaining a homogeneous concrete mix with an Abrams cone slump more than zero. Otherwise, the variation intervals should be narrowed.

Combination of all values that can take a factor in the frame of an experiment is called its variation range. In planning matrix (Table of planned experiments), the factors are given in coded form. The central or so-called zero point X_{io} is assumed to be the main varying level, and its variation interval is denoted as ΔX_i. By adding or subtracting the variation interval value to or from the value of the factor, located on the main level, the lower and upper variation level values are obtained. These values are denoted by (+1) or (+) for the upper factor level and by (-1) or (-) for the lower one.

Relationship between natural and coded factors values (X_i and x_i, respectively) can be determined as follows:

$$x_i = \frac{X_i - X_{io}}{\Delta X_i} \tag{2.7}$$

Selection of varying intervals depends on the research goals and opportunities, as well as on specific production conditions. Variation intervals for linear and incomplete quadratic dependencies are usually smaller, compared to full quadratic ones. As wider is the studied factor's range, linear dependence of the factor's output parameters on the factor itself becomes less probable. Variation intervals of the main technological factors for linear and quadratic equations that are generally applied for choice of optimum concrete mixtures compositions are presented in Table 2.3.

Table 2.3. Factors and variation intervals

Factors	Variation intervals, % of the main level, for dependencies	
	Linear and incomplete quadratic	Quadratic
Cement-water ratio, C/W	15 - 20	25 - 40
Water content, W, l/m^3	5 - 8	5 - 20
Mineral admixtures content, Ad, kg/m^3	20 - 50	20 - 100
Portion of sand in the mix of aggregates, r	5 - 10	5 - 15
Maximum dimension of crushed stone (gravel), D_{max}, mm	20 - 40	20 - 80
Sand fineness modulus, M_{fn}	20 - 25	30 - 50
Duration of previous exposure τ_{exp}, min	30 - 50	30 - 100
Duration of isothermal heating τ_{is}, hours	20 - 40	20 - 100
Total duration of heat processing for optimal structure of regime parameters τ_t, hours	20 - 30	20 - 50
Temperature of isothermal heat T_{is}, ^0C	8 - 10	8 - 25
Temperature rise velocity V, ^0C/hour	20 - 30	20 - 50
Ultimate cement strength R_{cem}, MPa	15 - 25	15 - 25

Conditions of experiment planning should be summarized in a special table, an example of which is given in Table. 2.4. Two-level plans are used to create linear dependencies. For quadratic dependencies, three-level plans and plans with higher number of levels are used.

Table 2.4. An example of planned experiments conditions for selection of composite additive composition including plasticizers and hardening accelerator

Factors		Variation levels			Variation interval
Natural form	Coded form	-1	0	+1	
C/W	x_1	1,4	2	2,6	0,6
Content of technical lignosulphonate (LST) in dry matter, % of cement mass	x_2	0	0,2	0,4	0,2
Content of nitrite-nitrate of calcium (NNC), % of cement mass	x_3	0	2	4	2

To avoid systematic errors and to obtain uniform distribution and eliminate undesirable effects on the entire experiment (fluctuations in humidity and temperature, small changes of aggregates grain distribution, etc.), the tests should be conducted not in the manner provided in the matrix but in some random (randomized) order.

2.2. CREATING LINEAR AND INCOMPLETE QUADRATIC MODELS

In studies of linear and partial (incomplete) quadratic dependencies, full factorial experiment (FFE) and fractional replicas are usually used.

In FFE experiments, planning is carried out at two levels— the upper (+1) and lower (-1). Experiments plans that are used allow implementation of all applicable non-recurring test options for different factors number. The number of experiments N depends on the number of factors k and is equal to 2^k: for example, for two factors - $2^2 = 4$, for three - $2^3 = 8$, for four - $2^4 = 16$ for five - $2^5 = 32$, etc. Assume that it is required to find a regression equation, describing the dependence of the concrete properties indicators (y) on factors x_1 and x_2 using the hypothesis that their influence has a linear nature. In this case, the FFE matrix has the form presented in Table 2.5. A scheme for obtaining FFE matrices for cases when the factors number k is between 2 and 5 is given in Table 2.6.

Table 2.5. FFE matrix for a 2^2 plan

Plan points u	Factors		Interaction	Output parameter
	x_1	x_2	x_1x_2	y
1	+1	+1	+1	y_1
2	+1	-1	-1	y_2
3	-1	+1	-1	y_3
4	-1	-1	+1	y_4

The tests results are processed by mathematical statistics methods, deriving the relationship between output parameters and factors that affect them, in a form of linear or partial quadratic regression equations.

In a common form for k factors:

$$\hat{y}_i = b_0 + \sum_{i=1}^{k} b_i \tilde{o}_i + \sum_{i \neq j} b_{ij} \tilde{o}_i \tilde{o}_j \qquad (2.8)$$

For example,

- for two factor experiment:
$$\hat{y}_i = b_0 + b_1x_1 + b_2x_2 + b_{12}x_1x_2 \qquad (2.9)$$

- for five factor experiment:
$$\hat{y}_i = b_0 + b_1x_1 + b_2x_2 + b_3x_3 + b_4x_4 + b_5x_5 + b_{12}x_1x_2 + b_{13}x_1x_3 +$$
$$+b_{14}x_1x_4 + b_{15}x_1x_5 + b_{23}x_2x_3 + b_{24}x_2x_4 + b_{25}x_2x_5 + b_{34}x_3x_4 + \qquad (2.10)$$
$$+b_{35}x_3x_5 + b_{45}x_4x_5$$

In a FFE with increasing the factors number, the number of experiments significantly increases. In some cases, at the first stage of research, i.e., preliminary assessment of factor's influence degree, the accuracy is less important and decreasing the accuracy level can yield significantly reduce the experiments number. For this reason, fractional replicas (1/2, 1/4, 1/8, etc.), obtained by dividing the FFE experiments amount by 2, 4, 8, are used.

Matrix fractional replicas are received by replacing the higher-order interactions in the FFE matrix (from the triple - $x_1 x_2 x_3$, etc.) by new variables. These interactions are usually insignificant.

Table 2.6. FFE matrix for $k = 2 \dots 5$

Plan points	Factors				
u	x_1	x_2	x_3	x_4	x_5
1	+1	+1	+1	+1	+1
2	+1	-1	+1	+1	+1
3	-1	+1	+1	+1	+1
4	-1	-1	+1	+1	+1
5	+1	+1	-1	+1	+1
6	+1	-1	-1	+1	+1
7	-1	+1	-1	+1	+1
8	-1	-1	-1	+1	+1
9	+1	+1	+1	-1	+1
10	+1	-1	+1	-1	+1
11	-1	+1	+1	-1	+1
12	-1	-1	+1	-1	+1
13	+1	+1	-1	-1	+1
14	+1	-1	-1	-1	+1
15	-1	+1	-1	-1	+1
16	-1	-1	-1	-1	+1
17	+1	+1	+1	+1	-1
18	+1	-1	+1	+1	-1
19	-1	+1	+1	+1	-1
20	-1	-1	+1	+1	-1
21	+1	+1	-1	+1	-1
22	+1	-1	-1	+1	-1
23	-1	+1	-1	+1	-1
24	-1	-1	-1	+1	-1
25	+1	+1	+1	-1	-1
26	+1	-1	+1	-1	-1
27	-1	+1	+1	-1	-1
28	-1	-1	+1	-1	-1
29	+1	+1	-1	-1	-1
30	+1	-1	-1	-1	-1
31	-1	+1	-1	-1	-1
32	-1	-1	-1	-1	-1

The number of experiments in fractional replica corresponds to 2^{k-p}, where p is the replica fraction. For example, a seven-factor FFE includes $2^7 = 128$

and a 1/2 replica is $2^{7-1} = 64$, 1/4 replica is $2^{7-2} = 32$, 1/8 replica is $2^{7-3} = 16$ experiments, etc. Assume that it is required to study the influence of five factors: x_1, x_2, x_3, x_4 and x_5. For obtaining a half – replica 2^{5-1}, it is possible to take a FFE 2^4, and the interaction of factors x_1, x_2, x_3, x_4 can be replaced by factor x_5 (Table 2.7). In this case, the number of tests is reduced by 50%, compared to the 2^5 FFE (Table 2.6).

The coefficient b_0, can be determined as:

$$b_0 = \frac{\sum_1^N y_u}{N}, \text{ or} \qquad (2.11)$$

$$b_0 = \frac{\sum_1^N \overline{y}_u}{N}, \qquad (2.12)$$

where N is the number of points of the plan; y_u is the experimental value of the output parameter at the plan points $u_1 \; ... \; u_n$; $\overline{y}_u$ is the average output parameter at the plan point u for the case, when $\overline{y}_u = \frac{\sum_1^r y_{ui}}{r}$, i.e., for repeated tests; r is the number of repeated experiments according to rows of the matrix.

The coefficients of linear members in the equations can be determined using the following formulas:

$$b_i = \frac{\sum_{i=1}^N x_{iu} y_u}{N} \text{ or} \qquad (2.13)$$

$$b_i = \frac{\sum_{i=1}^N x_{iu} \overline{y}_u}{N}, \qquad (2.14)$$

where x_{iu} is the value of factor i in the matrix row of experiment u.

The paired interactions coefficients are obtained as:

$$b_{ij} = \frac{\sum\limits_{u=1}^{N} x_{iu}\, x_{ju}\, y_u}{N} \quad \text{or} \tag{2.15}$$

$$b_{ij} = \frac{\sum\limits_{u=1}^{N} \tilde{o}_{iu}\, \tilde{o}_{ij}\, \overline{y}_u}{N} \tag{2.16}$$

where x_{ju} is the value of factor j in experiment u.

Table 2.7. A matrix of a 2^{5-1} fractional factorial plan

Plan points	Factors				
u	x_1	x_2	x_3	x_4	x_5
1	+1	+1	+1	+1	+1
2	+1	+1	+1	-1	-1
3	+1	+1	-1	+1	-1
4	+1	+1	-1	-1	+1
5	+1	-1	+1	+1	-1
6	+1	-1	+1	-1	+1
7	+1	-1	-1	+1	+1
8	+1	-1	-1	-1	-1
9	-1	+1	+1	+1	-1
10	-1	+1	+1	-1	+1
11	-1	+1	-1	+1	+1
12	-1	+1	-1	-1	-1
13	-1	-1	+1	+1	+1
14	-1	-1	+1	-1	-1
15	-1	-1	-1	+1	-1
16	-1	-1	-1	-1	+1

Creating the model is completed, and the model itself can be used for decision-making process only after the algebraic calculation of coefficients estimates will be complemented by a statistical (regression) analysis. At the first stage of regression analysis, the mean square errors S {b_i} of models coefficients estimates are obtained. The coefficients are considered to be significant if the calculated value of Student's t–criterion t_c is higher than its table value corresponding to a given significance level and number of degrees of freedom. The critical coefficient's estimates value, below which the calculated assessment of b_i can with risk α be considered insignificant (i.e., equal to zero) is obtained.

At the second stage, the hypothesis adequacy (experimental data relevance) between the polynomial model and all significant regression coefficients is tested. For this reason, the minimizing sum of squares, known in regression analysis as residual, is used. To check the adequacy, a zero hypothesis is formulated, and if it is recognized as credible according to the Fisher's F criterion, the model describes the process adequately to the experiment. From the engineering viewpoint, it means that the model provides results $\bar{y}$ with an average error being $\sqrt{F}$ times greater than the experimental.

Statistical analysis of equations is carried out:

- in case of duplication of research by matrix rows—the average output parameters value;
- without duplication—for additional research at the main level.

The arithmetic mean value of the output parameter $\bar{y}_u$ is obtained:

a) in case of duplication of research by matrix rows by the following formula:

$$\bar{y}_u = \frac{\sum_{i=1}^{r} y_{ui}}{r} = \frac{y_{u1} + y_{u2} + ... y_{ur}}{r} \tag{2.17}$$

where r – number of repeated experiments in the matrix row;

b) while conducting experiments in zero points by the formula:

$$\bar{y}_0 = \frac{\sum_{i}^{n_0} y_{ou}}{n_o} \tag{2.18}$$

where n_0 – number of zero points.

The reproducibility dispersion $S^2_{\{y\}}$ of the output parameter is obtained:

a) in case of duplication of research by matrix rows by the following formula:

$$S_{\{y\}}^2 = \frac{\sum\limits_{u=1}^{N}\sum\limits_{i=1}^{r}(y_{ui} - \bar{y}_u)^2}{N(r-1)} \tag{2.19}$$

where $\sum\limits_{i=1}^{r}$ – sum by matrix rows, $\sum\limits_{u=1}^{N}$ – sum by matrix columns, N – total number of plan points.

b) while conducting experiments in zero points by the formula:

$$S_{\{y\}}^2 = \frac{\sum\limits_{1}^{n_0}(y_{0u} - \bar{y}_0)}{(n_0 - 1)}. \tag{2.20}$$

Standard deviations of the output parameters are calculated:

a) in case of duplication of research by the following formula –

$$S_{\{y\}} = \sqrt{\frac{\sum\limits_{u=1}^{N}\sum\limits_{i=1}^{r}(y_{oi} - \bar{y}_u)^2}{N(r-1)}}, \tag{2.21}$$

b) while conducting experiments in zero points by the formula—

$$S_{\{y\}} = \sqrt{\frac{\sum\limits_{1}^{n_0}(y_{0u} - \bar{y}_u)}{n_0 - 1}}. \tag{2.22}$$

The mean square error in determining the coefficients, coefficients is obtained:

a) for linear and incomplete quadratic equations in case of duplicate research as:

$$S_{\{b_0\}} = S_{\{b_i\}} = S_{\{b_{ij}\}} = \frac{S_{\{y\}}}{\sqrt{N}}, \tag{2.23}$$

b) while conducting experiments in zero points $S_{\{y\}}$ should be replaced

by $S_{\{y_0\}}$, where y_0 is the output parameter for the factors values at zero (main) level.

The calculated value of Student's t-criterion (tc) for each coefficient of regression equations is found as:

$$t_{c\{b_0\}} = \frac{|b_o|}{S_{\{b_o\}}} \tag{2.24}$$

$$t_{c\{b_i\}} = \frac{|b_i|}{S_{\{b_i\}}} \tag{2.25}$$

$$t_{c\{b_{ij}\}} = \frac{|b_{ij}|}{S_{\{b_{ij}\}}} \tag{2.26}$$

The coefficients are considered to be significant if the calculated value of Student's t-criterion t_c is higher than its table value (Table 1, Appendices), depending on a given significance level and number of degrees of freedom $f_{\{y\}}$. In technological research, the significance level is assumed to be equal to 0.05 or 0.1, and the number of degrees of freedom can be determined as follows:

a) in case of duplication of research by matrix rows using equation:
$f_{\{y\}} = N(r-1);$ \hfill (2.27)

b) while conducting experiments in zero points:
$f_{\{y\}} = n_0 - 1.$ \hfill (2.28)

If the coefficient is insignificant, it can be rejected without re-calculation of others. After assessing the significant coefficients, the adequacy of equations should be checked. It is done by obtaining the adequacy dispersion, the design value of Fisher's criterion and comparing the last with the table values according to the below-described procedure.

The adequacy dispersion S_{ad}^2 is obtained

a) for linear and incomplete quadratic equations in case of duplicate research as:

$$S_{ad}^2 = \frac{\sum_{u=1}^{N}(\hat{y} - y_u)^2}{N - m} \tag{2.29}$$

b) in case of duplication of research by matrix rows using equation:

$$S_{ad}^2 = \frac{r}{N - m} \sum_{u=1}^{N}(\hat{y}_u - \overline{y}_u)^2 \tag{2.30}$$

where m is the number of significant coefficients, $\hat{y}$ is the value of output parameter calculated by regression equations.

To assess the adequacy of regression equations, F-criterion (Fisher's criterion) is used. The design value of this criterion is obtained as follows:

for $S_{ad}^2 < S_{\{y\}}^2$

$$F_c = \frac{S_{ad}^2}{S_{\{y\}}^2} \tag{2.31}$$

for $S_{ad}^2 > S_{\{y\}}^2$

$$F_c = \frac{S_{\{y\}}^2}{S_{ad}^2} \tag{2.32}$$

where $S_{\{y\}}^2$ is the reproducibility dispersion of the output parameter.

The table value of the F-criterion (Ft) is obtained depending on the given confidence probability (significance level) and the number of degrees of freedom (Table 1, Appendices). In concrete technology, the significance level is usually equal to 95%. The number of degrees of freedom of the adequacy dispersion fad for linear and incomplete quadratic equations is calculated using the following formula:

$$f_{ad} = N - m. \qquad (2.33)$$

where m is the number of significant coefficients in the equation.

The number of degrees of freedom for the table F-criterion value for complete quadratic equations in presence of zero points in the plan is obtained as follows:

$$f_{ad} = N - m - (n_0 - 1). \qquad (2.34)$$

where n_0 is the number zero points.

F – criterion (F_t) is obtained taking into account the number of degrees of freedom f_{ad} and $f_{\{y\}}$.

The equation is adequate for the given confidence probability level if $F_c > F_t$. If the equation is inadequate, it means that during the experiments, gross errors occurred or the chosen polynom does not fully reflect the investigated dependence. In such cases, it is necessary to repeat the experiments, to change the variation intervals, or a different plan should be applied.

Example 2.2. It is required to create a mathematical model for concrete compressive strength (R_{cmp}) in 28-day age with the aim of correcting the cement-water ratio C/W (x_1) for concrete with ultimate compressive strength of 15…30 MPa and cone slump (Sl) of 3...5 cm depending on ultimate cement strength R_{cem} (x_2), fineness modulus M_{fn} (x_3) and content of clay and dust-like particles, Q_p (x_4) in the sand.

As initial materials, Portland cement with mineral admixtures, quartz sand and crushed granite stone fraction 5...20 mm were used. The experiments were carried out according to plan FFE 2^4 (Table 2.6). The experiment planning conditions are given in Table 2.8.

Table 2.8. Conditions of experiment planning

Factor		Variation level			Variation
Natural	Coded	-1	0	+1	interval
C/W	x_1	1.4	2.0	2.6	0.6
R_{cem}, MPa	x_2	38.8	45.3	51.8	6.5
M_{fn}	x_3	1.4	2.2	3	0.8
Q_p, %	x_4	1	3	5	2

At each plan point, three concrete samples were prepared and tested in order to obtain their compressive strengths. The matrix of experiments planning and experimental values of concrete strength are presented in Table 2.9. The coefficients of regression equations were determined according to Eqs. (2.11 - 2.16):

$$b_0 = \frac{436.1}{16} = 27.3; \quad b_1 = \frac{178.5}{16} = 11.2; \quad b_{23} = \frac{2.7}{16} = 0.2$$

where 436.1; 178.5 and 2.7 are the data from Table 2.9; 16 is the number of tests according to the matrix rows.

Table 2.9. Planning matrix and experimental values of concrete strength

Plan points	Factors				R_{cmp}, MPa			Mean strength value, MPa
	x_1	x_2	x_3	x_4	y_1	y_2	y_3	
1	+1	+1	+1	+1	44.2	43	43.6	43.6
2	+1	+1	+1	-1	49	49.6	47.5	48.7
3	+1	+1	-1	+1	42	39.6	41.1	40.9
4	+1	+1	-1	-1	45	44	44.2	44.4
5	+1	-1	+1	+1	31.8	32	32.8	32.2
6	+1	-1	+1	-1	35	34	35.4	34.8
7	+1	-1	-1	+1	29.6	31	30.6	30.4
8	+1	-1	-1	-1	32	33	31.9	32.3
9	-1	+1	+1	+1	20.6	22	20.7	21.2
10	-1	+1	+1	-1	22.5	21	21.9	21.8
11	-1	+1	-1	+1	20.8	19.6	18.4	19.6
12	-1	+1	-1	-1	21.2	19	20.7	20.3
13	-1	-1	+1	+1	12.9	11	11.8	11.9
14	-1	-1	+1	-1	13.7	13	11.1	12.6
15	-1	-1	-1	+1	11	10.4	9.8	10.4
16	-1	-1	-1	-1	12	11	10.3	11.1
Sum	-	-	-	-	-	-	-	436.1
								$b_0 = 27.3$

In a similar way were also obtained other coefficients of regression equations given in Table. 2.10.

Table 2.10. Coefficients of regression equations

Parameters for determining the coefficients									
For linear members				For interactions					
$\overline{y}x_1$	$\overline{y}x_2$	$\overline{y}x_3$	$\overline{y}x_4$	$\overline{y}x_1x_2$	$\overline{y}x_1x_3$	$\overline{y}x_1x_4$	$\overline{y}x_2x_3$	$\overline{y}x_2x_4$	$\overline{y}x_3x_4$
43.6	43.6	43.6	43.6	43.6	43.6	43.6	43.6	43.6	43.6
48.7	48.7	48.7	-48.7	48.7	48.7	-48.7	48.7	-48.7	-48.7
40.9	40.9	-40.9	40.9	40.9	-40.9	40.9	-40.9	40.9	-40.9
44.4	44.4	-44.4	-44.4	44.4	-44.4	-44.4	-44.4	-44.4	-44.4
32.2	-32.2	32.2	32.2	-32.2	32.2	32.2	-32.2	-32.2	32.2
34.8	-34.8	34.8	-34.8	-34.8	34.8	-34.8	-34.8	34.8	-34.8
30.4	-30.4	-30.4	30.4	-30.4	-30.4	30.4	30.4	-30.4	-30.4
32.3	-32.3	-32.3	-32.3	-32.3	-32.3	-32.3	32.3	32.3	32.3
-21.1	21.1	21.1	21.1	-21.1	-21.1	-21.1	21.1	21.1	21.1
-21.8	21.8	21.8	-21.8	-21.8	-21.8	21.8	21.8	-21.8	-21.8
-19.6	19.6	-19.6	19.6	-19.6	19.6	-19.6	-19.6	19.6	19.6
-20.3	20.3	-20.3	-20.3	-20.3	20.3	20.3	-20.3	-20.3	20.3
-11.9	-11.9	11.9	11.9	11.9	-11.9	-11.9	-11.9	-11.9	11.9
-12.6	-12.6	12.6	-12.6	12.6	-12.6	12.6	-12.6	12.6	-12.6
-10.4	-10.4	-10.4	10.4	10.4	10.4	-10.4	10.4	-10.4	-10.4
-11.1	-11.1	-11.1	-11.1	11.1	11.1	11.1	11.1	11.1	11.1
$\Sigma=$ 178.5	$\Sigma=$ 84.7	$\Sigma=$ 17.3	$\Sigma=$ -15.9	$\Sigma=$ 11.1	$\Sigma=$ 7.8	$\Sigma=$ -10.3	$\Sigma=$ 2.7	$\Sigma=$ -4.1	$\Sigma=$ -2.3
b_1=11.2	b_2=5.3	b_3=1.1	b_4=-1	b_{12}=0.9	b_{13}=0.5	b_{14}=-0.6	b_{23}=0.2	b_{24}=-0.3	b_{34}=-0.1

The statistical characteristics were determined as follows:

a) the reproducibility dispersion $S_{\{y\}}^2$ was found using Eq. (2.19):

$$S_{\{y\}}^2 = \frac{30.16}{16(3-1)} = 0.943 \; ;$$

The calculations results are presented in Table 2.11.

b) the standard deviation $S_{\{y\}}$ was obtained using Eq. (2.21):

$$S_{\{y\}} = \sqrt{0.943} = 0.97$$

c) the mean square error $S\{b\}$ for the coefficients of regression equations was calculated using Eq. (2.23):

$$S\{_{b0}\} = S_{\{bi\}} = S_{\{bij\}} = -\frac{0.97}{\sqrt{16}} = 0.2$$

Table 2.11. Calculation of the reproducibility dispersion by matrix rows

Plan points u	$(y_1 - \overline{y}_n)^2$	$(y_2 - \overline{y}_n)^2$	$(y_3 - \overline{y}_n)^2$	$\sum S_{\{y\}}^2$
1	$(45.2\text{-}43.6)^2$=2.56	$(43.0\text{-}43.6)^2$=0.36	$(42.6\text{-}43.6)^2$=1	2.9
2	$(49\text{-}48.7)^2$=0.09	$(49.6\text{-}48.7)^2$=0.81	$(47.5\text{-}48.7)^2$=1.44	2.34
3	$(42.0\text{-}40.9)^2$=1.21	$(39.6\text{-}40.9)^2$=1.69	$(41.1\text{-}40.9)^2$=0.04	2.94
4	$(45.0\text{-}44.4)^2$=0.36	$(44 - 44.4)^2$=0.16	$(44.2\text{-} 44.4)^2$=0.04	0.56
5	$(31.3\text{-}32.2)^2$=0.81	$(32\text{-}32.2)^2$=0.04	$(33.3\text{-}32.2)^2$=1.21	2.06
6	$(35\text{-}34.8)^2$=0.04	$(34\text{-}34.8)^2$=0.64	$(35.4\text{-}34.8)^2$=0.36	1.04
7	$(29.6\text{-}30.4)^2$=0.64	$(31\text{-}30.4)^2$=0.36	$(30.6\text{-}30.4)^2$=0.04	1.04
8	$(32\text{-}32.3)^2$=0.09	$(33\text{-}32.3)^2$=0.49	$(31.9\text{-}32.3)^2$=0.16	0.74
9	$(20.6\text{-}21.1)^2$=0.25	$(22\text{-}21.1)^2$=0.81	$(20.7\text{-}21.1)^2$=0.16	1.22
10	$(22.5\text{-}21.8)^2$=0.49	$(21\text{-}21.8)^2$=0.64	$(21.9\text{-}21.8)^2$=0.01	1.14
11	$20.8\text{-}19.6)^2$=1.44	$(19.6\text{-}19.6)^2$=0	$(18.4\text{-}19.6)^2$=1.44	2.88
12	$(21.2\text{-}20.3)^2$=0.81	$(19\text{-}20.3)^2$=1.69	$(20.7\text{-}20.3)^2$=0.16	2.66
13	$(12.9\text{-}11.9)^2$=1	$(11\text{-}11.9)^2$=0.81	$(11.8\text{-}11.8)^2$=0.01	1.82
14	$(13.7\text{-}12.6)^2$=1.21	$(13\text{-}12.6)^2$=0.16	$(11.1\text{-}12.6)^2$=2.25	3.62
15	$(11\text{-}10.4)^2$=0.36	$(10.4\text{-}10.4)^2$=0	$(9.8\text{-}10.4)^2$=0.36	0.72
16	$(12\text{-}11.1)^2$=0.81	$(11\text{-}11.1)^2$=0.01	$(10.3\text{-}11.1)^2$=0.64	1.46
Sum 30.16				

d) Student's t-criterion

The table value of t_t is obtained using Table 1 in the Appendices for significance level α=0.05 (P = 5%). In the current example, t_t = 2.04 for f_y =N (r-1) = 16(3-1) = 32.

Lowest coefficients are chosen from Table. 2.10. The calculated values of t_c (Eq.2.26) are:

$$t_{34} = \frac{0.1}{0.24} = 0.42 \; ; \; t_{13} = \frac{0.5}{0.24} = 2.08 \; ; \; t_{23} = \frac{0.2}{0.24} = 0.83$$

$$t_{14} = \frac{0.6}{0.24} = 2.5 \; ; \; t_{24} = \frac{0.3}{0.24} = 1.25$$

As t_{23}, t_{24} and t_{34} are less than t_t, coefficients, b_{23}, b_{24} and b_{34} are not significant (these coefficients are underlined in Table 2.10). Taking into account the coefficients significance, the mathematical model of concrete strength (in terms of coded variables) will take the following form:

$$\hat{y} = 27.3 + 11.2x_1 + 5.3x_2 + 1.1x_3 - x_4 + 0.7x_1x_2 + 0.5x_1x_3 - 0.6x_1x_4 \quad (2.35)$$

For checking the adequacy of the obtained regression equation, the design value of $\hat{y}$ for each matrix row is found according to Table.2.10.

For example, for the first row:

$$\hat{y} = 27.3+11.2(+1)+5.3(+1)+1.1(+1)+0.7(+1)(+1)+0.5(+1)(+1)$$
$$-0.6(+1)(+1) = 44.5 \text{ MPa}$$

For all other rows, similar calculations are performed, and the results are given in Table 2.12. After that, sum of squares for deviations of calculated data are obtained.

Table 2.12. Calculation of adequacy dispersion

Plan points	$\hat{y}_u$	$\bar{y}_u$	$\hat{y}_u - \bar{y}_u$	$(\hat{y}_u - \bar{y}_u)^2$	Plan points	$\hat{y}_u$	$\bar{y}_u$	$\hat{y}_u - \bar{y}_u$	$(\hat{y}_u - \bar{y}_u)^2$
1	44.5	43.6	-0.9	0.81	9	20.9	21.1	0.2	0.04
2	47.7	48.7	1	1	10	21.7	21.9	0.1	0.01
3	41.3	40.9	-0.4	0.16	11	18.5	19.6	1.1	1.21
4	44.5	44.4	-0.1	0.01	12	20.5	20.7	-0.2	0.04
5	32.5	32.2	0.3	0.09	13	11.7	11.9	0.2	0.04
6	35.6	34.8	-0.8	0.64	14	12.1	12.6	0.5	0.25
7	29.3	30.4	1.1	1.21	15	10.5	10.4	0.1	0.01
8	32.5	32.3	0.2	0.04	16	11.3	11.1	-0.2	0.04
					Sum				5.6

The adequacy dispersion is obtained by Eq. (2.29):

$$S_{ad}^2 = \frac{3 \cdot 5.6}{16 - 8} = 2.1,$$

Here, 5.6 is the sum from Table 2.12; three is the number of experiments according to matrix row; eight is the number of significant coefficients (Table 2.10).

The calculated value of Fisher's criterion is:

$$F_c = \frac{2.1}{0.943} = 2.13$$

where 0.943 is the value of reproducibility dispersion.

The table value of F_t is obtained using linear interpolation according to Table 2 in the Appendices. For $f_1 = 16(3 - 1) = 32$ and $f_2 = 16 - 8 = 8$ $F_t = 2.29$.

As $F_c < F_t$. the regression equation is adequate. The equation that was obtained can be used for creating a nomogram (Figure 2.5).

At the stage when a nomogram is prepared, the design value of C/W is obtained for different values of the investigated factors.

The equation is solved for x_1:

$$0.6x_1x_4 - 0.7x_1x_2 - 0.5x_1x_3 - 11.2x_1 = 27.3 + 5.3x_2 + 1.1x_3x_4 - x_4 - \hat{y},$$

$$x_1 = \frac{27.3 + 5.3x_2 + 1.1x_3x_4 - x_4 - \hat{y}}{0.6x_4 - 0.7x_2 - 0.5x_3 - 11.2}.$$

Before calculating the required value of x_1, the coded varying factors values should be first found. For example, for $R_{cem} = 50$ MPa, $M_{fn} = 1.8$ and $Q_p = 2\%$:

$$x_2 = \frac{R_{cem} - 45.3}{6.5} = \frac{50 - 45.3}{6.5} = 0.72,$$

$$x_3 = \frac{M_{fn} - 2.2}{0.8} = \frac{1.8 - 2.2}{0.8} = -0.5,$$

$$x_4 = \frac{Q_p - 3}{2} = \frac{2 - 3}{2} = -0.5.$$

where 6.5, 0.8 and 2 are variation intervals (Table 2.8).

Hence, for concrete with $y = 40$ MPa

$$x_1 = \frac{27.3 + 5.3 \cdot 0.72 - 1.1(-0.5) - (-0.5) - 40}{0.6(-0.5) - 0.7 \cdot 0.72 - 0.5(-0.5) - 11.2} = 0.67.$$

The natural value of C/W can be found from the following relationship:

$$x_1 = \frac{C/W - 2}{0.6}, \quad C/W = 0.6x_1 + 2 = 0.6 \cdot 0.67 + 2 = 2.4,$$

where 2 and 0.6 are the main level and variation interval of C/W, respectively (Table 2.8). In a similar way, the C/W for other values of R_{cem}, M_{fn}, Q_p and R_{cmp} can be obtained. Based on the obtained data, it is possible to prepare a nomogram that can be further used to get the values of C/W for known values of concrete strength and varying factors (Figure 2.5). For example, for concrete with R_{cmp}=40 MPa, R_{cem}= 50 MPa (node a), M_{fn}=2.2 (node b) and Q_p = 3% (node c) C/W = 2.4 (node d).

Example 2.3. Required to design concrete mix compositions with cone slump of 2, 4 and 6 cm. The concrete compressive strength (four hours after steaming at a temperature of 80^0C, regime 2+3+6+2 hours) should be 60 and 70% of ultimate 28-day strength - 20 MPa. The cement used for the concrete mix production is Portland cement of ultimate strength 40 MPa. Crushed granite stone fraction 5...10 mm, quartz sand with M_{fn} = 1.6 are used as aggregates.

The calculated contents of cement (C), water (W) and part of sand in the aggregates mix (r) per 1 m^3 of concrete with cone slump of 4 cm are: C=283 kg; W = 180 kg; r = 0.35. Taking into account these values, the variation intervals and levels for realization of a typical matrix for two variables are taken (Table 2.13). Contents of sand (S) and crushed stone (Cr.S) for each matrix point are calculated according to the absolute volumes method.

After calculating the regression coefficients and estimating their significance, the regression equations for cone slump $\hat{y}_l$ and compressive strength (four hours after steaming) $\hat{y}_2$ with 95% probability level are obtained:

$$\hat{y}_1 = 3.6+1.3x_2. \tag{2.36}$$

$$\hat{y}_2 = 12.5+1.62x_1-0.6x_2. \tag{2.37}$$

Table 2.13. Conditions of experiment planning

Factor		Variation levels			Variation interval
Natural	Encoded	-1	0	+1	
Cement content, kg/m³	x_1	255	283	311	28
Water content. kg/m³	x_2	188	198	208	10

The water quantity required for providing the given cone slump of the concrete mix can be found from equation (2.36). The content of cement, providing the required strength for the given water content, can be obtained from equation (2.37). Table 2.14 presents calculated contents of concrete mix components.

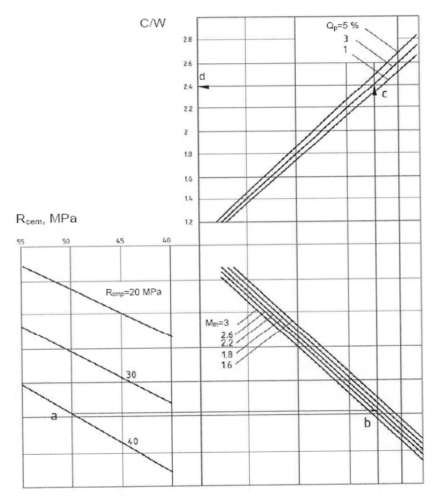

Figure 2.5. Nomogram for obtaining C/W for various values of concrete compressive strength depending on investigated factors.

Table 2.14. Compositions of concrete mixes with ultimate 28-day strength of 20 MPa

Cone slump, cm	Compressive strength (four hours after steaming), MPa	Materials contents per 1 m³ of concrete, kg			
		C	W	S	Cr.S
2	12	259	188	754	1250
2	14	294	188	724	1250
4	12	279	203	687	1250
4	14	314	203	667	1250
6	12	297	218	642	1250
6	14	332	218	612	1250

2.3. SECOND-ORDER PLANNING AND OBTAINING QUADRATIC MODELS

In resolving building technological problems, most dependence can be adequately described by second-order polynomial equations. These equations can be used as mathematical models for description of the response surface near the optimum, or so-called stationary, region.

A second order mathematical model has the following form:

$$\hat{y} = b_0 + \sum_{i=1}^{k} b_i\, x_i + \sum_{i=1}^{k} b_{ij}\, x_i x_j + \sum_{i=1}^{k} b_{ii}\, x_i^2 \qquad (2.38)$$

where k is the factors number.

The task is to determine the coefficients estimates of the model according to the results of the planned experiment.

The main requirement of the second-order plan is that the last should allow obtaining individual, not combined, regression coefficients estimates. It requires that the number of different experiments should not be less than the number of coefficients in the model that is equal to the number of combinations of k +2 by two, i.e.,

$$N \geq \frac{(k+2)(k+1)}{2} = C_{k+2}^2 \qquad (2.39)$$

In addition, each factor should be varied by at least at three levels.

Plans of complete quadratic dependences are obtained by adding to the kernel (i.e., FFE or fractional replicas) additional points or so-called "star points" and in some cases even zero points with appropriate variation interval (shoulder), denoted by α.

In concrete and reinforced concrete technology, research practices are most often used rotatable plans, Box-Behnken plans as well as two-, three-, four- and five-factorial plans that are very similar to the so-called D–optimal plans.

Planning is optimal when associated with relatively simple computations and when it provides the estimates of regression coefficients that are independent and are determined with equal and minimal dispersion.

Table 2.15. A rotatable plan matrix for $k = 3$

Plan points u		Planning matrix			Variables' squares			Factors interaction			Output parameter y_i
		x_1	x_2	x_3	x^2_1	x^2_2	x^2_3	x_1x_2	x_1x_3	x_2x_3	
N_1	1	+1	+1	+1	+1	+1	+1	+1	+1	+1	y_1
	2	+1	+1	-1	+1	+1	+1	+1	- 1	- 1	y_2
	3	+1	- 1	+1	+1	+1	+1	- 1	+1	- 1	y_3
	4	+1	- 1	- 1	+1	+1	+1	- 1	- 1	+1	y_4
	5	- 1	+1	+1	+1	+1	+1	- 1	- 1	+1	y_5
	6	- 1	+1	- 1	+1	+1	+1	- 1	+1	- 1	y_6
	7	- 1	- 1	+1	+1	+1	+1	+ 1	- 1	- 1	y_7
	8	- 1	- 1	- 1	+1	+1	+	+1	+1	+1	y_8
N_α	9	+1.682	0	0	+2.828	0	0	0	0	0	y_9
	10	-1.682	0	0	+2.828	0	0	0	0	0	y_{10}
	11	0	+1.682	0	0	+2.828	0	0	0	0	y_{11}
	12	0	-1.682	0	0	+2.828	0	0	0	0	y_{12}
	13	0	0	+1.682	0	0	+2.828	0	0	0	y_{13}
	14	0	0	-1.682	0	0	+2.828	0	0	0	y_{14}
n_0	15	0	0	0	0	0	0	0	0	0	y_{15}
	16	0	0	0	0	0	0	0	0	0	y_{16}
	17	0	0	0	0	0	0	0	0	0	y_{17}
	18	0	0	0	0	0	0	0	0	0	y_{18}
	19	0	0	0	0	0	0	0	0	0	y_{19}
	20	0	0	0	0	0	0	0	0	0	y_{20}

The dispersion of the optimization parameter providing the regression equation should not depend on rotation of coordinate system in the center of the plan. The above-mentioned criteria are satisfied if the planning has the properties of orthogonality and ratability.

Planning is called orthogonal if all scalar product of vectors-columns of the plan matrix is zero. Plan's orthogonality allows obtaining estimates for the regression coefficients that are independent each of the other.

One of the major drawbacks of orthogonal plans is that a model obtained on the basis of orthogonal plan provides feedback on various factor space directions with varying accuracy.

Planning is called rotatable if it is invariant to the coordinate system's rotation. It means that the information, contained in the regression equation, should be evenly distributed ("smeared") on a hyper-sphere (on a sphere for k = 3, a circle for $k = 2$) with a radius r ($r^2 = \Sigma x_i^2$). If planning is rotatable, the optimization parameter's values have minimal dispersions at different points of the factor's space. Additionally, the dispersions are equal at equal distance from the center of the experiment (origin) in any direction.

Table 2.15 presents an example of a second-order plan matrix for three factors (k=3). Rotatable plans for k= 4 and k= 5 are shown in the Appendices (Tables 3, 4).

Coefficients of regression equations for rotatable plans can be obtained as follows:

$$b_0 = T_1(O_y) - T_2 \sum_{i=1}^{k} (iiy) \tag{2.40}$$

$$b_i = T_3(iy) \tag{2.41}$$

$$b_{ii} = T_4(iiy) + T_5 \sum_{i=1}^{k} (iiy) - T_2(O_y) \tag{2.42}$$

$$b_{ij} = T_6(ijy) \tag{2.43}$$

In Eqs. (2.40...2.43):

$$(O_y) = \sum_{u=1}^{N} y_u; \ (iy) = \sum_{u=1}^{N} x_{iu} \, y_u \tag{2.44}$$

$$(ijy) = \sum_{u=1}^{N} x_{iy} x_{ju} \, y_u; \quad (iiy) = \sum_{u=1}^{N} (x_{iy})^2 y_u \tag{2.45}$$

T_1–T_6 are parameters for calculation of regression equations' coefficients. Values of parameters T for rotatable plans are given in the Table 2.16. In cases when influence of two factors is investigated, but one of them is more important, so-called hexagonal rotatable plans are used. In such plans, the first factor varies on five levels, and the second, just on three (Table 2.17).

Corresponding coefficients can be found using the following equations:

$$b_0 = (O_y) - \sum_{u=1}^{k}(iiy) \qquad (2.46)$$

$$b_i = 0{,}333(iy) \qquad (2.47)$$

$$b_{ii} = 0{,}667(iiy) + 0{,}833\sum_{u=1}^{k}(iiy) - (O_y) \qquad (2.48)$$

$$b_{ij} = 1{,}333\,(ijy) \qquad (2.49)$$

Table 2.16. Values of parameters T for rotatable plans

Number of factors k	Plan's Core N_1	Number of zero points n_0	T_1	T_2	T_3	T_4	T_5	T_6
2	2^2	5	0.2	0.1	0.125	0.125	0.0187	0.25
3	2^3	6	0.1663	0.0568	0.0732	0.0625	0.0069	0.125
4	2^4	7	0.1428	0.0357	0.0417	0.0312	0.0037	0.0625
5	2^{5-1}	6	0.1591	0.0341	0.0417	0.0312	0.0028	0.0625

Three level Box-Behnken's plans are very close to rotatable ones. A matrix of Box-Behnken's plan for $k=3$ is given in Table 5 (in the Appendices), matrices for $k=4$ and $k=5$ are presented in the Appendices (Tables 6,7). Corresponding coefficients of regression equations are obtained as follows:

$$b_0 = \frac{\sum_{i=1}^{n_0} y_0}{n_0} \qquad (2.50)$$

$$b_i = T_3(iy) \qquad (2.51)$$

$$b_{ii} = T_4(iiy) + T_5\sum_{u=1}^{k}(iiy) - T_2(O_y) \qquad (2.52)$$

$$b_{ij} = T_6(iiy) \qquad (2.53)$$

Table 2.17. Rotatable hexagonal plan

Plan points u	Planning matrix		Variables' squares		Interaction	Output Parameter
	x_1	x_2	x_1^2	x_2^2	$x_1 x_2$	y_i
1	-1	0	+1	0	0	y_1
2	+1	0	+1	0	0	y_2
3	0.5	0.865	0.25	0.75	0.43	y_3
4	0.5	-0.865	0.25	0.75	-0.43	y_4
5	-0.5	0.865	0.25	0.75	-0.43	y_5
6	-0.5	-0.865	0.25	0.75	0.43	y_6
7	0	0	0	0	0	y_7

Calculated values of parameters $T_2 - T_6$ are given in Table 2.18.

It is effective to use Box-Behnken's plans for solving problems, in which the sequence of x_i in multifactorial situation should be stabilized in a group of experiments. If the aim of the experiment is to find a quadratic model with most accurate estimates of parameters, then using a D-optimal plan is effective. For two- and three-factorial experiments, three-level plans are used (Tables 2.19, 2.20). For four- and five-factorial experiments, it is more effective to use three-level compositional B_4- and B_5-type plans with properties close to D-optimal ones. Such plans can be obtained by adding "star" points with $\alpha=\pm 1$ to the FFE or to the fractional replica. In order to obtain a Ha_5 plan, one more zero point is added (Tables 8-10 in the Appendices).

Table 2.18. Values of parameters T in Box-Behnken plan

Number of factors k	Total number of points N	Number of zero points n_0	T_2	T_3	T_4	T_5	T_6
3	15	3	0.1667	0.125	0.25	0.625	0.25
4	27	3	0.5	0.0833	0.125	0.0208	0.25
5	46	6	0.5	0.0625	0.0833	0.0104	0.625

Table 2.19. A three-level plan matrix for $k = 2$

Plan points u		Planning matrix		Variables' squares		Factors interaction $x_1 x_2$	Output parameter y_i
		x_1	x_2	x^2_1	x^2_2		
N_1	1	+1	+1	+1	+1	+1	y_1
	2	+1	-1	+1	+1	-1	y_2
	3	-1	+1	+1	+1	-1	y_3
	4	-1	-1	+1	+1	+1	y_4
N_α	5	+1	0	+1	0	0	y_5
	6	-1	0	+1	0	0	y_6
	7	0	+1	0	+1	0	y_7
	8	0	-1	0	+1	0	y_8
n_0	9	0	0	0	0	0	y_9
	10	0	0	0	0	0	y_{10}
	11	0	0	0	0	0	y_{11}

Table 2.20. A three-level plan matrix for $k = 3$

Plan points u		Planning matrix			Variables' squares			Factors interaction			Output parameter y_i
		x_1	x_2	x_3	x^2_1	x^2_2	x^2_3	$x_1 x_2$	$x_1 x_3$	$x_2 x_3$	
N_1	1	+1	+1	+1	+1	+1	+1	+1	+1	+1	y_1
	2	+1	+1	-1	+1	+1	+1	+1	-1	-1	y_2
	3	+1	-1	+1	+1	+1	+1	-1	+1	-1	y_3
	4	+1	-1	-1	+1	+1	+1	-1	-1	+1	y_4
	5	-1	+1	+1	+1	+1	+1	-1	-1	+1	y_5
	6	-1	+1	-1	+1	+1	+1	-1	+1	-1	y_6
	7	-1	-1	+1	+1	+1	+1	+1	-1	-1	y_7
	8	-1	-1	-1	+1	+1	+1	+1	+1	+1	y_8
N_α	9	+1	0	0	+1	0	0	0	0	0	y_9
	10	-1	0	0	+1	0	0	0	0	0	y_{10}
	11	0	+1	0	0	+1	0	0	0	0	y_{11}
	12	0	-1	0	0	+1	0	0	0	0	y_{12}
	13	0	0	+1	0	0	+1	0	0	0	y_{13}
	14	0	0	-1	0	0	+1	0	0	0	y_{14}
n_0	15	0	0	0	0	0	0	0	0	0	y_{15}
	16	0	0	0	0	0	0	0	0	0	y_{16}
	17	0	0	0	0	0	0	0	0	0	y_{17}

Table 2.21. Values of parameters T in three – level plans for $k = 2 ... 3$

Factors number k	Plan type	T_1	T_2	T_3	T_4	T_5	T_6
2	Two-factorial	0.2632	0.1579	0.1667	0.5	-0.1053	0.25
3	Three-factorial	0.1832	0.0704	0.1	0.5	-0.1268	0.125

Coefficients b_0, b_i , b_{ii}, b_{ij} of the regression equations are obtained according to Eqs. (2.40...2.45). The calculated values of parameters $T_1 - T_6$ are given in Table 2.21, 2.22.

The regression equations, obtained using D-optimal plans, provide equal prediction accuracy of the output parameter in a region, defined by unit radius (from the zero point).

Table 2.22. Values of parameters T in three-level plans B_4, B_5 and Ha_5

Factors number	Plan type	T_1	T_2	T_3	T_4	T_5	T_6
4	B_4	0.2292	0.0625	0.0556	0.5	-0.1042	0.0625
5	B_5	0.1588	0.0332	0.0294	0.5	-0.0918	0.0312
5	Ha_5	0.138	0.0303	0.0556	0.5	-0.0909	0.0625

Choosing a plan depends on the task nature and on the possibility of varying the factors at the assumed levels. For problems with at least one hard-driven factor, i.e., a factor for which providing its natural value at all variation levels is complicated (for example cement strength, normal consistency of cement paste, etc.), it is recommended to use plans with minimum number of variation levels, two- and three-factorial plans at three levels or such plans as B_4, B_5 and Ha_5. For free factor's variation (additives consumption, hardening duration, etc.) rotatable plans can be used. Using a rotatable plan is most appropriate in cases where it is desirable to get the value of output parameters out the limits of +1 ...- 1.

When conducting experiments using three-level plans, special attention should be paid to the tests' accuracy in the "star" points.

If the quadratic dependences inadequately describe the process, adequacy can be achieved by replacing the value of one or several factors by their logarithms, inverse function, expressing the factors in an exponential form of or by other means. For direct calculations and creating graphs and nomograms, the regression equations that were obtained should be transformed into polynomials with natural factors' values using Eq. (2.7).

Carrying out the experiment is inevitably associated with errors because the investigated dependences and processes are probabilistic in nature, and the obtained equations represent them with some degree of probability. Therefore, statistical analysis, aimed at assessing the significance of the equations' coefficients and checking the equations' adequacy, is a mandatory stage. A general procedure for such statistical analysis of first- and second-order regression equations is the same.

Assessment of coefficients' significance for second-order regression equations is carried out like for linear ones using Eqs. 2.24...2.26. For complete quadratic equations when experiments are duplicated by the matrix rows, the mean square error in determining of the coefficients can be obtained as follows:

$$S_{\{b_o\}} = T_7 S_{\{y_u\}} \tag{2.54}$$

$$S_{\{b_i\}} = T_8 S_{\{y_u\}} \tag{2.55}$$

$$S_{\{b_{ii}\}} = T_9 S_{\{y_u\}} \tag{2.56}$$

$$S_{\{b_{ij}\}} = T_{10} S_{\{y_u\}} \tag{2.57}$$

The values of $T_7...T_{10}$ are obtained according to Table 2.23.

For complete quadratic equations, the calculated values of Student's t-criterion, t_c, for coefficients b_0, b_i and b_{ij} is correspondingly calculated using Eqs. (2.24...2.26), and coefficients b_{ii} are found as:

$$t_{c\{bii\}} = \frac{|b_{ii}|}{S_{\{b_{ii}\}}} \tag{2.58}$$

Calculation of t_c should begin from the coefficients with minimum absolute value.

When second-order plans are used, the coefficients of quadratic members in the equation are usually not excluded, even if they are not significant.

For complete quadratic equations, the adequacy dispersion can be found as

$$S_{ad}^2 = \frac{\sum\limits_{u=1}^{N}\left(\hat{y} - y_u\right)^2}{N - m - (n_{ou} - 1)} \qquad (2.59)$$

$$S_{ad}^2 = \frac{\sum\limits_{u=1}^{N}\left(\hat{y}_u - y_u\right)^2}{N - m} \qquad (2.60)$$

When tests are duplicated by the matrix rows

$$S_{ad}^2 = \frac{r}{N - m(n_{ou} - 1)} \sum\limits_{u=1}^{N}\left(\hat{y}_u - \bar{y}_u\right)^2 \qquad (2.61)$$

$$S_{ad}^2 = \frac{r}{N - m} \sum\limits_{u=1}^{N}\left(\hat{y}_u - \bar{y}_u\right)^2 \qquad (2.62)$$

Here, m is the number of significant coefficients, including b0; nou is the number of zero points of the matrix; ŷu is the calculated value of the output parameter in row u.

If the plan has zero points, the dispersion S_{ad}^2 can be obtained using Eq. 2.59 and 2.61, otherwise Eqs. 2.60 and 2.62 should be used.

Example 2.4. It is required to build a nomogram for regulating the C/W (x_2) of a concrete mixture according to its water content W (x1), superplasticizer quantity Sp (x4) and cement ultimate 28-day strength Rcem (x_3).

According to the defined problem, the variation range of the technological factors is set (Table 2.24).

In order to develop nomograms, a mathematical model, describing the dependence of concrete strength Rc, MPa, on the taken factors should be found. As it follows from Table 2.24, for the selected variation levels, the investigated dependence is likely to have a nonlinear nature. A B4 plan is assumed for carrying out the experiments.

The experiments planning matrix and the calculated parameters for obtaining the regression equations' coefficients are given in Table 2.25.

Table 2.23. Design parameters for obtaining mean square errors at determining the second order regression equations coefficients

Plan type	Factors number K	Total number of points N	Number of zero points n_{ou}	T_7	T_8	T_9	T_{10}
Rotatable	2	13	5	0.4472	0.3536	0.3793	0.5
	3	20	6	0.4078	0.2706	0.2634	0.3536
	4	31	7	0.378	0.2041	0.187	0.25
	5	32	6	0.3989	0.2041	0.1846	0.25
Same, hexagonal	2	7	1	1	0.5774	1.2247	1.1547
Box-Behnken	3	15	3	0.5774	0.3536	0.5204	0.5
	4	27	3	0.5774	0.2887	0.433	0.5
	5	46	6	0.4082	0.25	0.3385	0.5
Two-factorial three-level	2	11	3	0.513	0.4083	0.6282	0.5
Three-factorial three-level	3	17	3	0.4279	0.3162	0.6109	0.3536
B_4	4	24	0	0.4787	0.2357	0.6212	0.25
B_5	5	42	0	0.3985	0.1715	0.639	0.1768
Ha_5	5	27	1	0.3716	0.2357	0.6396	0.25

1. Obtain the Regression Equations Coefficients

a) The free member b0 can be calculated using Eq. (2.40):

$$b_0 = 0.2292 \cdot 1282 - 0.0625 \, (947.9 + 945.5 + 947.8 + 943.1) = 57.28,$$

where   0,2292 and 0,0625 are coefficients according to Table 2.22; 1282, 947.9, 945.5, 947.8 and 943.1 are sums according to Table.2.25 and 2.26.

b) Coefficients of the linear members are calculated using Eq. (2.41):

$$b_3 = 0.0556 \cdot 130.4 = 7.24,$$

where   130.4 is the sum from Table 2.25;
           0.0556 is a coefficient from Table 2.22.

Coefficients b1, b2, b4 can be obtained in a similar way.
c) The coefficients of the quadratic members are calculated using Eq. (2.42).

$b_{22} = 0.5 \cdot 945.5 - 0.1042 (947.9 + 945.5 + 947.8 + 943) - 0.0625 \cdot 1282 = -1.66$,

where 945.5, 947.8, 947.9 and 943.1 are sums from Table 2.26; 0.5,
    -0.1042 and 0.0625 are coefficients from Table 2.22.

Table 2.24. Conditions of experiment planning

Factors		Variation levels			Variation interval
Natural	Coded	-1	0	+1	
W, kg/m^3	x_1	160	190	220	30
C/W	x_2	1.5	2.5	3.5	1
R$_{cem}$, MPa	x_3	49.4	58.75	68.1	9.35
Sp,% of cement mass (calculated for dry substance)	x_4	0	0.25	0.5	0.25

Coefficients b_{11}, b_{33}, b_{44} can be obtained in a similar way.
d) Coefficients of the interactions are calculated using Eq. (2.43)

$b_{12} = 0.0625 (-22.1) = -1.38$,

where (-22.1) is sum from Table 2.26;

    0.0625 is a coefficient from Table 2.22.

Coefficients b_{13}, b_{14}, b_{23}, b_{24}, b_{34} can be obtained in a similar way (Table 2.26).

To check which coefficients are significant and further obtaining the adequacy of the equation, the reproducibility dispersion should be found. For this purpose, four experiments are additionally performed (Table2.27), fixing the factors at the main level.

Table 2.25. Planning matrix, experimental and design parameters

Plan points u	Factors				Experimental values y	Design parameters for calculation of determination the linear members coefficients			
	x_1	x_2	x_3	x_4		yx_1	yx_2	yx_3	yx_4
1	+1	+1	+1	+1	78.3	78.3	78.3	78.3	78.3
2	+1	+1	+1	-1	84.1	84.1	84.1	84.1	-84.1
3	+1	+1	-1	+1	60.8	60.8	60.8	-60.8	60.8
4	+1	+1	-1	-1	65.3	65.3	65.3	-65.3	-65.3
5	+1	-1	+1	+1	32.4	32.4	-32.4	32.4	32.4
6	+1	-1	+1	-1	34.6	34.6	-34.6	34.6	-34.6
7	+1	-1	-1	+1	22.8	22.8	-22.8	-22.8	22.8
8	+1	-1	-1	-1	26.1	26.1	-26.1	-26.1	-26.1
9	-1	+1	+1	+1	86.2	-86.2	86.2	86.2	86.2
10	-1	+1	+1	-1	89.9	-89.9	89.9	89.9	-89.9
11	-1	+1	-1	+1	66.4	-66.4	66.4	-66.4	66.4
12	-1	+1	-1	-1	69.7	-69.7	69.7	-69.7	-69.7
13	-1	-1	+1	+1	33.6	-33.6	-33.6	33.6	33.6
14	-1	-1	+1	-1	34.3	-34.3	-34.3	34.3	-34.3
15	-1	-1	-1	+1	23.8	-23.8	-23.8	-23.8	23.8
16	-1	-1	-1	-1	25.8	-25.8	-25.8	-25.8	-25.8
17	+1	0	0	0	55.6	55.6	0	0	0
18	-1	0	0	0	58.2	-58.2	0	0	0
19	0	+1	0	0	77.8	0	77.8	0	0
20	0	-1	0	0	33.6	0	-33.6	0	0
21	0	0	+1	0	65.7	0	0	65.7	0
22	0	0	-1	0	48.0	0	0	-48.0	0
23	0	0	0	+1	52.8	0	0	0	52.8
24	0	0	0	-1	56.2	0	0	0	-56.2
Sum					1282	-27.9	411.5	130.4	-28.9
Coefficients					$b_0 = 57.3$	$b_1 = -1.6$	$b_2 = 22.9$	$b_3 = 7.2$	$b_4 = -1.6$

2. Checking Significance of Regression Equations' Coefficients

a) The mean strength value in MPa in zero point is obtained using Eq. (2.18):

Table 2.26. Design parameters for calculation of regression equation coefficients

Plan points u	Parameters for calculation of coefficients for									
	squared members				interaction					
	yx_1^2	yx_2^2	yx_3^2	yx_4^2	yx_1x_2	yx_1x_3	yx_1x_4	yx_2x_3	yx_2x_4	yx_3x_4
1	78.3	78.3	78.3	78.3	78.3	78.3	78.3	78.3	78.3	78.3
2	84.1	84.1	84.1	84.1	84.1	84.1	-84.1	84.1	-84.1	-84.1
3	60.8	60.8	60.8	60.8	60.8	-60.8	60.8	-60.8	60.8	-60.8
4	65.3	65.3	65.3	65.3	65.3	-65.3	-65.3	-65.3	-65.3	65.3
5	32.4	32.4	32.4	32.4	-32.4	32.4	32.4	-32.4	-32.4	32.4
6	34.6	34.6	34.6	34.6	-34.6	34.6	-34.6	-34.6	34.6	-34.6
7	22.8	22.8	22.8	22.8	-22.8	-22.8	22.8	22.8	-22.8	-22.8
8	26.1	26.1	26.1	26.1	-26.1	-26.1	-26.1	26.1	26.1	26.1
9	86.2	86.2	86.2	86.2	-86.2	-86.2	-86.2	86.2	86.2	86.2
10	89.9	89.9	89.9	89.9	-89.9	-89.9	89.9	89.9	-89.9	-89.9
II	66.4	66.4	66.4	66.4	-66.4	66.4	-66.4	-66.4	66.4	-66.4
12	69.7	69.7	69.7	69.7	-69.7	69.7	69.7	-69.7	-69.7	69.7
13	33.6	33.6	33.6	33.6	33.6	-33.6	33.6	-33.6	-33.6	33.6
14	34.3	34.3	34.3	34.3	34.3	-34.3	34.3	-34.3	34.3	-34.3
15	23.8	23.8	23.8	23.8	23.8	23.8	-23.8	23.8	-23.8	-23.8
16	25.8	25.8	25.8	25.8	25.8	25.8	25.8	25.8	25.8	25.8
17	55.6	0	0	0	0	0	0	0	0	0
18	58.2	0	0	0	0	0	0	0	0	0
19	0	77.8	0	0	0	0	0	0	0	0
20	0	33.6	0	0	0	0	0	0	0	0
21	0	0	65.7	0	0	0	0	0	0	0
22	0	0	48	0	0	0	0	0	0	0
23	0	0	0	52.8	0	0	0	0	0	0
24	0	0	0	56.2	0	0	0	0	0	0
Sum	947.9	945.5	947.8	943.1	-22.1	-3.9	-6.1	+39.9	-9.1	+0.7
Coefficients	$b_{11} =$ -0.4	$b_{22} =$ -1.6	$b_{33} =$ -0.4	$b_{44} =$ -2.8	$b_{12} =$ -1.4	$b_{13} =$ -0.3	$b_{14} =$ -0.4	$b_{23} =$ 2.5	$b_{24} =$ -0.6	$b_{34} =$ -0.04

$$\bar{y}_0 = \frac{56.1 + 56.45 + 58.1 + 58.35}{4} = \frac{229}{4} = 57.25$$

b) The reproducibility dispersion in the zero point $S_{\{\bar{y}_0\}}$ is calculated according to Eq. (2.20):

$$S^2_{\{\bar{y}_0\}} = \frac{(57.25-56.1)^2 - (57.25-56.45)^2 + (57.25-58.1)^2 + (57.25-58.35)^2}{(4-1)} = \frac{3.9}{3} = 1.3$$

Table 2.27. Experimental and design results at zero points

Plan points U	Factors				$\hat{y}_{ou}$	$\bar{y}_o$	$\hat{y}_{ou} - \bar{y}_o$	$(\hat{y}_{ou} - \bar{y}_o)^2$
	x_1	x_2	x_3	x_4				
1	0	0	0	0	56.1		-1.14	1.31
2	0	0	0	0	56.45	57.25	-0.8	0.64
3	0	0	0	0	58.1		0.85	0.72
4	0	0	0	0	58.35		1.1	1.21
Sum					229			3.9

c) Standard deviation $S_{\{\bar{y}_0\}}$ is calculated using Eq. (2.22):

$$S_{\{\bar{y}_o\}} = \sqrt{1,3} = 1.14$$

d) The mean square errors $S_{\{b\}}$ of the regression coefficients (Eqs. 2.54...2.57) is:

$S_{\{b_o\}} = 0.4787 \cdot 1.14 = 0.55$,

$S_{\{b_i\}} = 0.2357 \cdot 1.14 = 0.27$,

$S_{\{b_{ii}\}} = 0.6212 \cdot 1.14 = 0.71$,

$S_{\{b_{ij}\}} = 0.25 \cdot 1.14 = 0.29$

where 0.4787, 0.2357, 0.6212 and 0.25 are taken according to Table 2.23.

e) Obtain Student's t-criterion.

The table value tt (following Table 1 in Appendices) for $\alpha = 0.05$ and $f_{\bar{y}_0} = 4-1 = 3$ is tt=3.18. The calculated values t_c are obtained using Eqs. (2.24... 2.26, 2.58), beginning from the regression equations coefficients with minimum absolute values:

$$t_1 = \frac{1.6}{0.27} = 5.92 \quad t_{12} = \frac{1.4}{0.29} = 4.83$$

$$t_{11} = \frac{0.4}{0.71} = 0.56 \quad t_{13} = \frac{0.3}{0.29} = 1.03$$

$$t_{22} = \frac{1.6}{0.71} = 2.25 \quad t_{14} = \frac{0.4}{0.29} = 1.38 \quad t_{33} = \frac{0.4}{0.71} = 0.56 \quad t_{23} = \frac{2.5}{0.29} = 8.62$$

$$t_{44} = \frac{2.8}{0.71} = 3.94 \quad t_{24} = \frac{0.6}{0.29} = 2.07$$

$$t_{34} = \frac{0.04}{0.29} = 0.14$$

As t_{13}, t_{14}, t_{24} and $t_{34} < t_t$, coefficients b_{13}, b_{14}, b_{24} and b_{34} are insignificant (their values are underlined in Table 2.26). The coefficients of quadratic members b_{11}, b_{22}, b_{33} are also insignificant, but they should not be removed from the model because all quadratic members' coefficients are related not just among themselves but also to a free member.

The regression equation for concrete strength has the form:

$$\hat{o} = 57.3 - 1.6x_1 + 22.9x_2 + 7.2x_3 - 1.6x_4 - 0.4x_1^2 - 1.6x_2^2 - 0.4x_3^2 - 2.8x_4^2 - (2.63)$$
$$-1.4x_1x_2 + 2.5x_2x_3$$

3. Determining the Regression Equation's Adequacy

a) Find the residual sum of deviations' squares that were previously calculated for each matrix row. With this aim, the calculated value of $\hat{y}$ is obtained using Eq. (2.61) by matrix rows. For example, for the first row:

$$\hat{o} = 57.3 - 1.6(+1) + 22.9(+1) + 7.2(+1) - 1.6(+1) - 0.4(+1)^2 - 1.6(+1)^2 - 0.4(+1)^2 -$$
$$2.8(+1)^2 - 1.4(+1)(+1) + 2.5(+1)(+1) = 80.1$$

Similar calculations are performed for all rows of the matrix. The calculated results are given in Table 2.28.

b) *The adequacy dispersion* S_{ad}^2 *according to Eq. (2.29) is*

$$S_{ad}^2 = \frac{21.9}{24-11} = 1.68$$

where 21.9 is the sum calculated using Table 2.28; twenty-four is the number of tests (N1+Nα); 11 is the number of significant coefficients in the regression Eq. (2.63).

c) *Fisher's F-criterion:*

The calculated value Fc is obtained according to Eq. (2.31). For the current example

$$F_c = \frac{1.68}{1.3} = 1.3$$

where 1.3 is the reproducibility dispersion $S_{\{\bar{y}\}}^2$ (see stage.2 b);

1.68 is the adequacy dispersion S_{ad}^2 (see stage 3 b);

Table 2.28. Calculation of adequacy dispersion

Plan points	y	$\hat{y}$	$y_u - \hat{y}$	$(y-\hat{y}_u)^2$	Plan points	y	$\hat{y}$	$y_u - \hat{y}$	$(y-\hat{y}_u)^2$
1	78.3	80.1	-1.8	3.24	13	33.6	32.5	1.1	1.21
2	84.1	83.3	0.8	0.64	14	34.3	32.5	1.8	3.24
3	60.8	60.7	0.1	0.01	15	23.8	23.1	0.7	0.49
4	65.3	63.9	1.4	1.96	16	25.8	26.3	-0.5	0.25
5	32.4	32.1	0.3	0.09	17	55.6	55.3	0.3	0.09
6	34.6	35.3	-6.7	0.49	18	58.2	58.5	-0.3	0.09
7	22.8	22.7	0.1	0.01	19	77.8	78.6	-0.8	0.64
8	26.1	25.9	0.2	0.04	20	33.6	32.8	0.8	0.64
9	86.2	86.1	0.1	0.01	21	65.7	64.1	1.6	2.56
10	89.9	89.3	0.6	0.36	22	48.0	49.7	-1.7	2.89
11	66.4	68.1	-1.7	2.89	23	52.8	52.9	-0.1	0.01
12	69.7	69.9	-0.2	0.04	24	56.2	56.1	0.1	0.01

The table value of F-criterion F_T is obtained according to Table 2 in the Appendices. For a confidence probability of 95%, $f_{y_o} = 4-1 = 3$ and $f_{ad} = 24 - 11 = 13$ $F_t = 8,7$ $\left(S^2_{\{\bar{y}_o\}} < S^2_{ad} \right)$.

As $F_c < F_t$, the regression equation is adequate and it can be used as a mathematical model of concrete strength for the given range of the investigated factor's variation.

4. Creating a Nomogram

When creating a nomogram to regulate the concrete composition, the calculated value of C/W (x_2) should be obtained for changing the investigated factors (x_1, x_3, x_4). With this aim, a polynomial equation of the following form is solved regarding x_2:

$$\hat{y} = b_0 + b_1 x_1 + b_2 x_2 + b_3 x_3 + b_4 x_4 + b_{11}x_1^2 + b_{22} x_2^2 +$$
$$+ b_{33} x_3^2 + b_{44} x_4^2 + b_{12} x_1 x_2 + b_{13} x_1 x_3 + b_{14} x_1 x_4 + \qquad (2.64)$$
$$+ b_{23} x_2 x_3 + b_{24} x_2 x_4 + b_{34} x_3 x_4$$

The equation can be represented as:

$$B x_2^2 + L x_2 + C = 0 \qquad (2.65)$$

Coefficients B and L, as well as the free member C are found by transforming Eq.(2.64):

$$ô = b_{22} x_2^2 + \left(b_2 + b_{12} x_1 + b_{23}x_3 + b_{24} x_4 \right)x_2 + b_0 +$$
$$b_1 x_1 + b_3 x_3 + b_4 x_4 + b_{11} x_1^2 + b_{33} x_3^2 + b_{44} x_4^2 + b_{13} x_1 x_3 + \qquad (2.66)$$
$$+ b_{14} x_1 x_4 + b_{34} x_3 x_4$$

Denoting $b_2 + b_{12} x_1 + b_{23} x_3 + b_{24} x_4 = L$
$$b_0 + b_1 x_1 + b_3 x_3 + b_4 x_4 + b_{11} x_1^2 + b_{33} x_3^2 +$$
$$+ b_{44} x_4^2 + b_{13} x_1 x_3 + b_{14} x_1 x_4 + b_{34} x_3 x_4 - \hat{y} = C$$

Eq. (2.66) is solved for x2:

$$x_2 = \frac{-L \pm \sqrt{L^2 + 4b_{22} \cdot C}}{2b_{22}}.$$

(2.67)

To obtain x2 using Eq. (2.67), the coded values x1, x3 and x4 are used:

$$x_1 = \frac{W - 190}{30}; \quad x_3 = \frac{R_{cem} - 58.75}{9.35}; \quad x_4 = \frac{Sp - 0.25}{0.25}$$

Then, turn to the natural values of C/W:

$$C / W = 2,5 + x_2.$$

(2.68)

For example, for concrete strength Rcmp = 40 MPa (W = 180 kg/m3; Rcem = 50 MPa; Sp = 0%) x1, x3 and x4 will be as follows:

$$x_1 = \frac{180 - 190}{30} = -0.33; \quad x_3 = \frac{50 - 58.75}{9.35} = -0.94;$$

$$x_4 = \frac{0 - 0.25}{0.25} = -1$$

and

$$L = 22.9 + (-1.4)(-0.33) + 2.5(-0.94) + 0(1) =$$
$$22.9 + 0.46 - 2.35 + 0 = 21.01$$

$$C = 57.3 + (-1.6)(-0.33) + 7.2(-0.94) + (-1.6)(-1) + 0(-0.33)^2 + 0(-0.94)^2 +$$
$$(-2.8)(-1)^2 + 0(-0.33)(-0.94) + 0(-0.33)(-1) + 0(-0.94)(-1) - 40 =$$
$$57.3 + 0.53 - 6.77 + 1.6 - 2.8 - 40 = 9.86$$

Coefficient b22 = -1,6 for x_2^2 is obtained according to Table 2.26:

$$x_2 = \frac{-21.01 + \sqrt{(21.02)^2 - 4(-1.6)9.86}}{2(-1.6)} = \frac{-21.01 \pm 22.46}{-3.2}$$

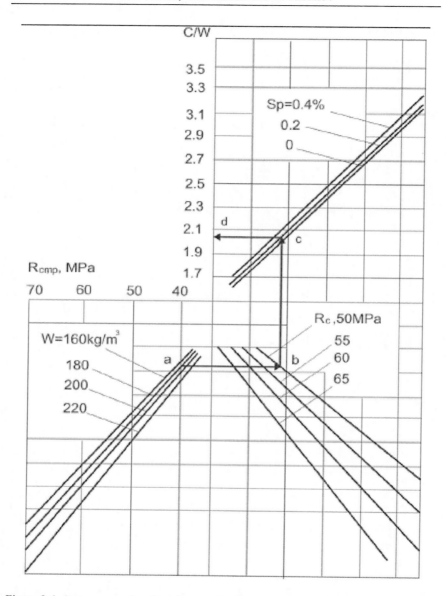

Figure 2.6. A nomogram for obtaining water-cement ratio for different ultimate concrete compressive strength, cement strength, water expenditure and content of Sp admixture.

$$x_2' = \frac{-21.01 - 22.46}{-3.2} = \frac{-43.47}{-3.2} = 13.59$$

$$x_2'' = \frac{-21.01 + 22.46}{-3.2} = \frac{1.45}{-3.2} = -0.453$$

Select $x_2'' = -0.453$, as $x_2' = 13.59$ has no physical sence ($C/W \geq 4$, that is practically not real for regular concrete).

C/W is obtained by Eq. (2.66):
C / W = 2.5 − 0.453 · 1 = 2.047.

For W=180 kg/m3, the cement content is

C = W · C / W = 180 · 2.047 = 368 kg/m3

A similar way allows finding C/W for other interactions of technological factors. For example:

- for Rcmp = 40 MPa; W = 165 kg/m3; Rcem = 50 MPa; Sp = 0,25 %; C/W = 1.972;
- for Rcmp = 60 MPa; W = 190 kg/m3; Rcem = 55 MPa; Sp = 0; C/W = 2.81, etc.

Based on the obtained data, a nomogram is created (Figure 2.6). It can be used in the production process if technological factors are changed for specifying the value of C/W and correcting the concrete composition.

For example, for concrete at Rcmp=40 MPa for W = 180 kg/m3 (node a) Rcem = 50 MPa (node b), Sp = 0,2 % (node c) C/W = 2.05 (node d). To construct the nomogram, a lot of calculations are required. Therefore, using computers for performing the calculations is recommended.

2.4. PLANNING EXPERIMENTS USING "COMPOSITION-PROPERTY" DIAGRAMS

When planning of experiment using "composition-property" diagrams, it should be taken into account that the components of the mix are dependent variables $t_{23} = \dfrac{Q2}{Q24} = Q8$. Therefore, special canonized polynomials are used:

$$t_{14} = \frac{0.6}{0.24} = 2.5 . \tag{2.69}$$

The number of b_i-coefficients in such polynomials equals $t_2 = \dfrac{Q3}{Q24} = 12$.

Composition-property diagrams, like, for example, state diagrams of silicate systems, are commonly represented in the simplex coordinates, or a convex shape, formed by a set of (m +1) independent points in an m-dimensional space with minimum vertices' number. For a plane, it is a triangle; in a three-dimensional space it is a tetrahedron, etc. The experiment-planning problem comes down to optimally placement of the experimental points on the simplex.

Scheffe has proposed plans in which the given number of points is uniform distributed on the simplex (simplex grid) (Figure 2.7).

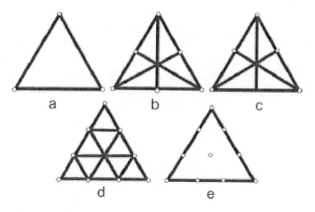

Figure 2.7. Simplex-grid plans (a—first-order, b—second-order, c—incomplete third-order, d—third-order, e—third-order (D-optimal)).

The coordinates of experimental points represent combinations:

$$x_i = 0,\ 1/n,\ 2/n,\ 1...$$

Formulas for calculating the coefficients of r-order polynomials for q-component materials are given below.

a) second-order polynomial:

$$y = \sum_{1 \le i \le q} b_i\, x_i + \sum_{1 \le i < k \le q} b_{ik}\, x_i\, x_k \qquad (2.70)$$

for r=2
$b_i = y_i;\ b_{ik} = 4y_{ik} - 2y_i - 2y_k;$
b) incomplete third-order polynomial:

$$y = \sum_{1 \le i \le q} b_i\, x_i + \sum_{1 \le i < k \le q} b_{ik}\, x_i\, x_k + \sum_{1 \le i < k < l \le q} b_{ikl}\, x_i\, x_k\, x_l \qquad (2.71)$$

for r=3
$b_i = y_i;\ b_{ik} = 4y_{ik} - 2y_i - 2y_k;$
$b_{ikl} = 27y_{ikl} - 12\,(y_i + y_{il} + y_{kl}) + 3\,(\,y_i + y_k + y_l\,);$

c) third-order polynomial:

$$y = \sum_{1 \le i \le q} b_i\, x_i + \sum_{1 \le i < k \le q} b_{ik}\, x_i x_k + \sum_{1 < i < k \le q} c_{ik} x_i x_k (x_i - x_k) + \sum_{1 \le l < k < l \le q} b_{ikl}\, x_i\, x_k\, x_l \qquad (2.72)$$

for r=3
$b_i = y_i;\ b_{ik} = \dfrac{9}{4}(y_{iik} + y_{ikk}\, y_i - y_k);$

$c_{ik} = \dfrac{9}{4}(3y_{iik} - 3y_{ikk}\, y_i - y_k);$

$b_{ikl} = 27\, y_{ikl} - \dfrac{27}{4}(y_{ikl} + y_{ikk} + y_{iil} + y_{ill} + y_{kkl} + y_{kll}) + \dfrac{9}{2}(y_i + y_j + y_k);$

In equations (2.70...2.72) y_i, y_{ikl}, y_{ik} are the values of the investigated characteristic for a composition, corresponding to the simplex top, center, mid rib, respectively.

The equation's adequacy is checked by t-criterion at the control point:

$$t = \frac{(\hat{y} - \bar{y})\sqrt{n}}{S\sqrt{n + \xi}}, \tag{2.73}$$

where $\bar{y}$ is the mean value of the characteristic obtained from n tests in a control point with dispersion S^2; ξ is a constant (Figure 2.8).

For second-order polynomials:

$$S^2_{\{y\}} = S^2 \left[\sum_{1 \le i \le q} \frac{a_i^2}{n_i} + \sum_{1 \le i < k \le q} \frac{a_{ik}^2}{n_{ik}} \right], \tag{2.74}$$

for $r = 2$

$a_i = x_i (2x_i - 1)$; $a_{ik} = 4x_i x_k$.

For incomplete third-order polynomials:

$$S^2_{\{y\}} = S^2 \left[\sum_{1 \le i \le q} \frac{b_i^2}{n_i} + \sum_{1 \le i < k \le q} \frac{b_{ik}^2}{n_{ik}} + \sum_{1 \le i < l < l \le q} \frac{b_{ikl}}{n_{ikl}} \right], \tag{2.75}$$

for $r = 3$

$$b_i^{=} x_4 = \frac{Q_p - 3}{2} = \frac{2 - 3}{2} = -0.5.$$

$b_{ik} = 4x_i x_k (3x_i + 3x_k - 2)$; $b_{ikl} = 27 x_i x_k x_l$.

For third-order polynomials:

$$s^2_{\{y\}} = s^2 \left[\sum_{1 \le i \le q} \frac{c_i^2}{n_i} + \sum_{1 \le i < k \le q} \frac{c_{iik}^2}{n_{iik}} + \sum_{1 \le i < k \le q} \frac{c_{ikk}}{n_{ikk}} + \sum_{1 \le i < k < l \le q} \frac{c_{ikl}^2}{n_{ikl}} \right] \tag{2.76}$$

for $r = 3$

$$c_i = \frac{1}{2} x_i (3x_i - 1)(3x_i - 2); \quad c_{iik} = \frac{9}{2} x_i x_k (3x_i - 1);$$

$$c_{ikk} = \frac{9}{2} x_i x_k (3x_k - 1); \quad c_{ikl} = 27 x_i x_k x_l.$$

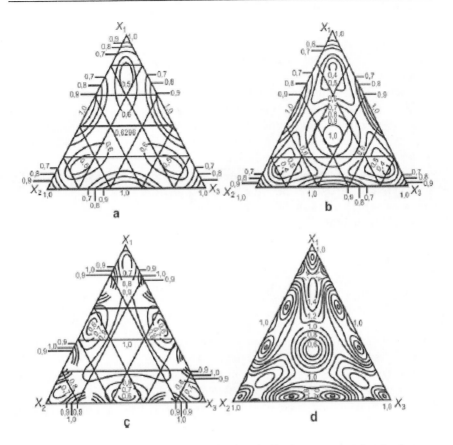

Figure 2.8. Projections of ξ for polynomials of Scheffe plans a—second-order; b—incomplete third-order; c—third-order; d—fourth-order.

A common drawback of above-discussed plans is that most of the experimental points are located on the simplex's periphery. Thus, the information is not uniformly distributed in the investigated region. Systematic bias minimization plans (Draper-Lawrence plans) do not have such disadvantage.

If a local part of a composition-property diagram should be investigated, it is placed inside a local simplex (Figure 2.9). In order to go from the pseudo-components (z_1, z_2, z_3, …) of the certain composition to the input components (x_1, x_2, x_3 …), the following formula can be used:

$$x_i = x_{i1} + p_2 (x_{i2} - x_{i1}) + p_3 (x_{i3} - x_{i1}) + \ldots + p_q (x_{iq} - x_{i1}), \qquad (2.77)$$

where x_{ik} is the content of component i in a top z_k; $p_2 \ldots p_q$ are the pseudo-components' contents.

Joint effect of mixed (interdependent) and technological (independent) factors on the materials' properties can be assessed using a "composition-technology-property" diagrams. To describe the "composition-technology-property" systems, product models (product of the mixed and technological factors' polynomials) can be used.

With this aim, at each plan point of the simplex is realized additionally, for example, a three-level plan (or vice versa). If, for example, the model is represented by a product of the second-order polynomial of three mixture factors "V" and technological factor "x," it can be presented as:

$$\hat{y} = \left(b_{0A_1} + b_{1A_1} x + b_{11A_1} x^2 \right) V_1 + \left(b_{0A_2} + b_{1A_2} x + b_{11A_2} x^2 \right) V_2 + \ldots +$$
$$\left(b_{0A_{23}} + b_{1A_{23}} x + b_{11A_{23}} x^2 \right) V_2 V_3, \qquad (2.78)$$

where A are coefficients of the model Scheffe polynomial; b are coefficients, characterizing the changes of A due to any change of x.

Fixing the value of "x" in the model, it is possible to obtain a set of "composition-property" models for different values of the technological factor. Fixing the V_i factors, it is possible to get a normal polynomial of the varying technological factor.

Example 2.5. It is required to find the influence of the filler's grain composition (with fractions less than 0,315 mm) on compressive strength of vibropressed concrete (R_{cmp}).

The investigation was carried out using a simplex-grid Scheffe "mixture-property" plan for creating an incomplete third-order polynomial model (Table 11, Appendices). The filler was divided into three fractions: $v_1 = 0.315 \ldots 0.16$ mm; $v_2 = 0.16 \ldots 0.08$ mm and $v_3 \leq 0.08$ mm. Experimental results are given in Table 2.29. The following concrete composition was used: C (cement) = 300 kg/m^3; Ag (aggregates) =1750 kg/m^3; W/C (water-cement ratio) = 0,52...0,55 The content of filler was 40% of the aggregates mass. The vibropressure parameters were: pressure – 0.1 MPa, amplitude – 0.5 mm, frequency – 50 Hz, duration – 15 sec.

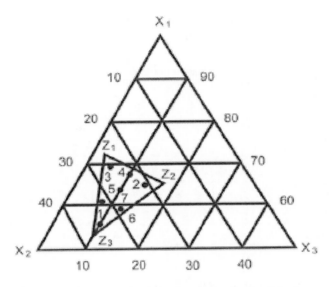

Figure 2.9. Experiment planning for investigating the local part of the "composition-property" diagram.

Using the experimental data, coefficients of the incomplete third-order polynomial can be obtained using Eg.2.71:

$b_i = y_i$;

$b_1 = 28.9$; $b_2 = 36.9$; $b_3 = 39.2$

$b_{ik} = 4y_{ik} - 2y_i - 2y_k$;

$b_{12} = 4y_{12} - 2y_1 - 2y_2 = 4 \cdot 32.9 - 2 \cdot 28.9 - 2 \cdot 36.9 = 0$;

$b_{13} = 4y_{13} - 2y_1 - 2y_3 = 4 \cdot 36.4 - 2 \cdot 28.9 - 2 \cdot 39.2 = 9.4$;

$b_{23} = 4y_{23} - 2y_2 - 2y_3 = 4 \cdot 37.1 - 2 \cdot 36.9 - 2 \cdot 39.2 = -3.8$;

$b_{ikl} = 27y_{ikl} - 12 (y_i + y_{il} + y_{kl}) + 3 (y_i + y_k + y_l)$;

$b_{123} = 27y_{123} - 12 (y_1 + y_{13} + y_{23}) + 3 (y_1 + y_2 + y_3) = 27 \cdot 36.0 - 12 \times$
$\times (28.9 + 36.4 + 37.1) + 3(28.9 + 36.9 + 39.2) = 10.2$.

As a result, the following regression equation is obtained:

$$R_{cmp} = 28.9V_1 + 36.9V_2 + 39.2V_3 + 9.4V_1V_3 - 3.8V_2V_3 + 10.2V_1V_2V_3 \quad (2.79)$$

Table 2.29. Influence of filler's grain composition on strength of vibropressed concrete

Plan points	Filler's grain composition			y_n	R_{cmp}, MPa
	v_1	v_2	v_3		
1	1	0	0	y_1	28.9
2	0	1	0	y_2	36.9
3	0	0	1	y_3	39.2
4	0.5	0.5	0	y_{12}	32.9
5	0.5	0	0.5	y_{13}	36.4
6	0	0.5	0.5	y_{23}	37.1
7	0.333	0.333	0.333	y_{123}	36.0

The adequacy of the obtained equation is checked by realizing the experiment for additional points.

Using the equation, a "filler's grain composition–strength" response, surface (Figure 2.10) and strength isolines on the mix triangle (Figure 2.11) are obtained.

Thus, increase in concrete strength of vibro-pressed concrete was observed to be proportional to the content of fractions <0.08 mm and 0.16...0.08 mm in the filler.

Example 2.5. It is required to create a model for compressive strength (R_{cmp}) of one-day age gypsum-slag-cement with superplasticizer and admixture of redispersible polymer, for determining the optimal composition of a dry building mix.

For solving the problem, a "mix-technology-property" plan is used. The following factors are assumed:

    a) mix (interdependent):
        V_1 – gypsum content (55%...75%);
        V_2 – content of grinded blast furnace slag (10%...30%);
        V_3 – Portland cement content (15%...35%);
    b) independent:
        x_1 – superplasticizer (Sp) (0...1,2%);
        x_2 – content of redispersible polymer (Rp) (0...2%)

Let's use a "mix-technology-property" plan for five factors. Planning matrix and experimental results are given in Table 2.30.

The regression equation for the output parameters, derived from the selected plan, has the following form:

$$y = A_1 V_1 + A_2 V_2 + A_3 V_3 + A_{12} V_1 V_2 + A_{13} V_1 V_3 + A_{23} V_2 V_3 +$$
$$+ (Ab)_{11} V_1 x_1 + (Ab)_{12} V_1 x_2 + (Ab)_{21} V_2 x_1 + (Ab)_{22} V_2 x_2 + (Ab)_{31} V_3 x_1 +$$
$$+ (Ab)_{32} V_3 x_2 + b_{12} x_1 x_2 + b_{11} x_1^2 + b_{22} x_2^2 \tag{2.80}$$

The equation's coefficients are calculated based on processing the obtained experimental data (Table 2.30) using the least square's method. The coefficient's value is equal to the sum of products of output parameters' values in the matrix (Table 2.30) and corresponding assessed calculated parameters (Table 2.31).

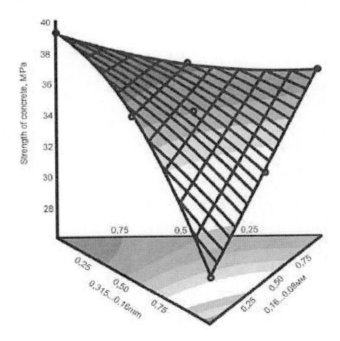

Figure 2.10. Response surface of the output parameter (compressive strength of vibropressed concrete (R$_{cmp}$, MPa)).

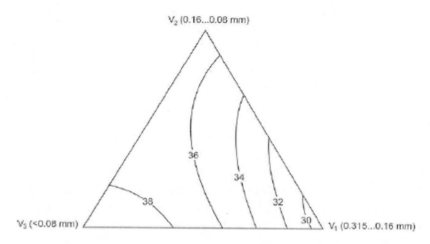

Figure 2.11. Relationship between compressive strength isolines for vibropressed concrete (Rcmp, MPa) and content of filler's fractions.

Table 2.30. Planning matrix and experimental results

No.	Coded factors					Natural factors					Rcmp, MPa, (1 day)
	V_1	V_2	V_3	x_1	x_2	Gypsum, %	Slag, %	Cement, %	Sp. %	Rp.%	
1	1	0	0	-1	-1	75	10	15	0	0	4.2
2	1	0	0	+1	+1	75	10	15	1.2	2	5.1
3	0	1	0	-1	-1	55	30	15	0	0	4.9
4	0	1	0	+1	-1	55	30	15	1.2	0	4.8
5	0	1	0	+1	+1	55	30	15	1.2	2	3.6
6	0	1	0	-1	+1	55	30	15	0	2	4.1
7	0	0	1	-1	-1	55	10	35	0	0	4.6
8	0	0	1	+1	0	55	10	35	1.2	1	4.4
9	0	0	1	-1	+1	55	10	35	0	2	4.0
10	0.5	0.5	0	0	-1	65	20	15	0.6	0	5.1
11	0.8	0.2	0	-1	+1	71	14	15	0	2	3.9
12	0.3	0	0.7	+1	+1	61	10	29	1.2	2	5.4
13	0.5	0	0.5	+1	-1	65	10	25	1.2	0	6.3
14	0.6	0	0.4	0	0	67	10	23	0.6	1	4.3
15	0	0.4	0.6	0	-1	55	18	27	0.6	0	5.3
16	0	0.5	0.5	-1	0	55	20	25	0	1	4.4

Thus, a mathematical model for standard mortar's strength is:

$$R_{cmp}=3.09V_1+1.96V_2+2.4V_3-4.67V_1V_2+0.16V_1V_3+3.74V_2V_3+$$
$$0.1V_1x_1-0.28V_1x_2+0.3V_2x_1-0.47V_2x_2+0.52V_3x_1-0.58V_3x_2-$$
$$0.56x_1x_2+0.05x_1^2+1.7x_2^2 \qquad (2.81)$$

To analyze the model, a diagram, including "mix" (interdependent) and "technological" (independent) factors, is created. The diagram can be represented a factorial quadrate in the vertices and at the center of which corresponding mix triangles are placed. The diagram can also be built as a mix triangle with corresponding factorial quadrates, located in each of its basic points.

For building triangular diagrams, for given values of x_1 and x_2 in corresponding points of a factorial quadrate, Eq. (2.81) is re-written in the following form:

$$y = b_1V_1 + b_2V_2 + b_3V_3 + b_{12}V_1V_2 + b_{13}V_1V_3 + b_{23}V_2V_3 + b_0 \qquad (2.82)$$

The calculated coefficients' values of Eq. 2.81 in corresponding points are presented in Table 2.32.

For building a factorial quadrate, Eq. (2.81) is adapted to the model of factors x_1 and x_2 for given values of V_1, V_2 and V_3.

For $V_1=V_2=V_3=0,333$, Eq. (2.81) takes the form:

$$R_{cmp} = 6.1+0.8x_1-0.37x_2+0.3x_1^2+0.67x_2^2-0.11x_1\,x_2. \qquad (2.83)$$

The response function according to Eq. (2.83) is given in Figure 2.12.

A general view for a "mixture-technology-property" diagram is shown in Figure 2.13. As it follows from the diagram, it is possible to reach a mortar's strength of 10 MPa and higher at maximum superplasticizer content of (0,6...1,2%), minimum admixture of redispersible polymer and also for gypsum, slag and Portland cement contents of 60...70%; 15...20% and 20...25%, respectively.

Table 2.31. A matrix for calculating the coefficients of the "mixture-technology-property" model

No.	Parameters for calculating the coefficients							
	A_1	A_2	A_3	A_{12}	A_{13}	A_{23}	$(Ab)_{11}$	$(Ab)_{12}$
1	0.36	-0.051	-0.054	-1.439	-0.807	0.221	-0.202	-0.294
2	0.55	-0.059	0.049	-0.932	-1.456	-0.094	0.397	0.104
3	-0.129	0.197	-0.061	-0.392	0.409	-0.783	-0.08	0.062
4	0.062	0.219	-0.045	-0.903	-0.064	-0.372	-0.025	0.045
5	-0.11	0.225	-0.04	0.456	0.328	0.106	-0.011	-0.005
6	0.17	0.335	0.144	-1.132	-0.65	-0.788	0.084	-0.047
7	-0.227	-0.122	0.145	0.663	0.334	-1.027	-0.059	0.07
8	0.337	0.3	0.655	-0.16	-1.937	-1.107	0.028	-0.032
9	0.093	-0.019	0.282	-0.675	-0.712	-0.413	0.066	-0.078
10	0.095	0.142	0.127	3.127	-0.445	-0.194	0.256	-0.252
11	-0.148	-0.222	-0.198	1.365	0.695	0.302	-0.401	0.393
12	0.554	-0.382	-0.237	0.918	1.795	0.887	-0.114	0.132
13	-0.285	-0.425	-0.381	0.62	1.334	0.58	0.23	-0.245
14	0.782	0.773	0.604	-1.45	1.206	-1.381	-0.14	0.139
15	0.124	0.081	0.269	-1.677	-0.761	1.575	0.117	0.112
16	-0.118	-0.078	-0.258	1.61	0.731	2.488	0.112	-0.108

No.	Parameters for calculating the coefficients						
	$(Ab)_{21}$	$(Ab)_{22}$	$(Ab)_{31}$	$(Ab)_{32}$	b_{12}	b_{11}	b_{22}
1	0	-0.001	0.037	0.087	0.04	0.026	0.066
2	0	0	-0.01	0.011	0.007	-0.037	-0.022
3	-0.249	-0.245	-0.008	0.007	0.104	0.036	0.014
4	0.249	-0.254	-0.015	-0.03	-0.118	0.09	-0.057
5	0.251	0.254	-0.019	0.026	0.115	0.029	-0.01
6	-0.251	0.246	0.059	-0.02	-0.111	-0.173	0.091
7	-0.001	-0.003	-0.233	-0.354	0.028	0.107	0.017
8	0	0.001	0.354	-0.051	-0.031	-0.016	-0.285
9	0.001	0.003	-0.199	0.345	-0.094	-0.104	0.121
10	0	-0.001	-0.015	0.065	0.039	-0.103	-0.038
11	0.001	0.002	0.023	-0.102	-0.001	0.162	0.059
12	-0.001	-0.005	0.145	0.239	0.144	0.124	0.261
13	0.001	0.004	0.045	-0.195	-0.118	0.31	0.113
14	0	0	-0.175	-0.006	-0.004	-0.431	-0.349
15	0	0.001	0.188	-0.059	-0.036	-0.466	0.384
16	0	-0.001	-0.181	0.057	0.034	0.447	-0.368

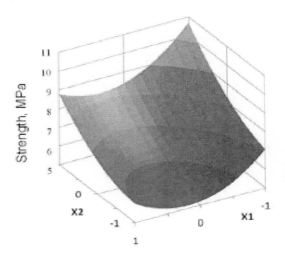

Figure 2.12. Response surface for mortar's strength according to Eq. (2.82).

Table 2.32. Coefficients of equations for triangular diagrams

Coefficients	Coefficients' values for given factors								
	$x_1=-1$ $x_2=-1$	$x_1=0$ $x_2=-1$	$x_1=+1$ $x_2=-1$	$x_1=-1$ $x_2=0$	$x_1=0$ $x_2=0$	$x_1=+1$ $x_2=0$	$x_1=-1$ $x_2=+1$	$x_1=0$ $x_2=+1$	$x_1=+1$ $x_2=+1$
b_1	7.92	10.09	12.26	7.53	9.70	11.87	7.13	9.30	11.48
b_2	3.54	3.39	3.25	3.04	2.90	2.75	2.55	2.40	2.25
b_3	3.57	3.96	4.34	3.33	3.71	4.10	3.09	3.47	3.86
b_{12}	1.69	1.69	1.69	1.69	1.69	1.69	1.69	1.69	1.69
b_{13}	2.47	2.47	2.47	2.47	2.47	2.47	2.47	2.47	2.47
b_{23}	2.72	2.72	2.72	2.72	2.72	2.72	2.72	2.72	2.72
b_0	0.61	0.72	0.82	0.04	0.04	0.04	0.82	0.72	0.61

2.5. ANALYSIS OF REGRESSION EQUATIONS AND SEARCHING OPTIMAL SOLUTIONS: A GENERAL SCHEME FOR EQUATIONS ANALYSIS

Linear models are easiest for analysis. The equations' coefficients sign indicate the factor's influence. A positive sign indicates that as the factor increases, the value of the corresponding output parameter is also increased, and negative sign means that as the factor increases, the value of the corresponding output parameter decreases. As the coefficient value is higher, the factor's influence becomes stronger.

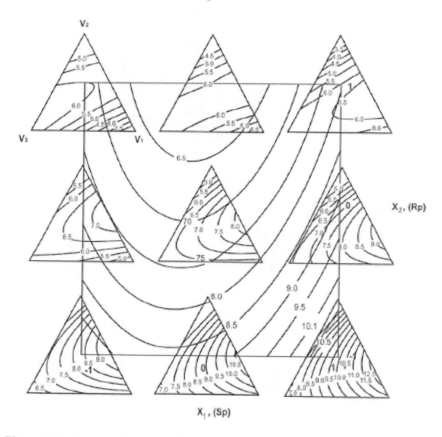

Figure 2.13. Diagram of gypsum-slag-cement mortar strength according to its composition.

If the output parameter should be maximum, values of all factors, for which coefficients b_i are positive, should be maximum and those for which coefficients b_i are negative should be minimal. The absolute values of regression equations' coefficients are increased with increasing the variation intervals.

In incomplete quadratic regression equations, the sign before the linear member coefficient corresponds to the change of the output parameters if other factors are assumed to be on the main level. Sign "+" before the interaction coefficient indicates that increasing the output parameter is possible only if all interacting factors are at the upper or lower level, and the sign "-" means that one factor is at the upper and the other at the lower level.

In quadratic equation, if all factors (except one) are on the main level, it can be transformed into a parabolic form:

$$\hat{y} = b_0 + b_1 x_1 + b_{11} x_1^2. \tag{2.84}$$

with an extremum (maximum or minimum) at the point $x_{1\text{ext}} = -b_1/2b_{11}$.
The absolute value of the coefficient b_i corresponds to the change speed of factor x_i.

A bi-factorial quadratic (complete) model:

$$\hat{y} = b_0 + b_1 x_1 + b_2 x_2 + b_{11} x_1^2 + b_{22} x_2^2 + b_{12} x_1 x_2 \tag{2.85}$$

depending on the values of coefficients b_i, b_{ii}, b_{ij} represents one of the second order surfaces: plane, parabolic cylinder, elliptical or hyperbolic paraboloid.

Projection of surface $\hat{y}$ onto the factors plane x_1 - x_2 is a line of equal output (isolines), where the output parameter $\hat{y}$ has a constant value, independent of the coordinates x_1 and x_2.

To obtain isolines of two-dimensional models (or sections of multidimensional models) on the factor plane x_1 - x_2, the following method can be used:

 – select a few sections of the factor space;
 – calculate equations for each section in the following form:

$$\hat{y} = b_0 + b_i x_i + b_{ii} x^2 \tag{2.86}$$

Solution of the obtained quadratic equation (2.86) is calculated by the formula:

$$x_i = -\frac{b_i}{2b_{ii}} \pm \sqrt{\frac{1}{b_{ii}}[\hat{y} - (b_0 - \frac{b_i^2}{4b_{ii}})]} \tag{2.87}$$

The coordinates of the proper points of given isolines are calculated by substituting values of $\hat{y}$ in Eq. (2.87).

V. Voznesensky has formulated and developed a methodology for ten typical problems that can be solved individually or jointly based on a polynomial model. The methodology enables obtaining:

1. The output parameter value ($\hat{y}$) for a point located within the investigated factorial space with coordinates that are different from those of the experimental plan points (interpolation problem);
2. Values of $\hat{y}$ for a point, located out of the investigated factorial space (extrapolation problem);
3. Geometrical figure (response surface), described by the model (analytical-geometrical problem);
4. Minimal possible value of $\hat{y}$ in the experiment's zone (minimization of $\hat{y}$);
5. Maximal possible value of $\hat{y}$ in the experiment's zone (maximization of $\hat{y}$);
6. Possible relations between the factor's values in the experiment's zone for a required level of $\hat{y}$ (control for a fixed $\hat{y}$);
7. Minimal values of factors, characterizing the resources' expenditure for a given object's quality (minimization of resources x_i for a fixed $\hat{y}$);
8. Data for creating control diagrams of $\hat{y}$ for two variable and one fixed factor (controlling $\hat{y}$ for two variable factors);
9. Data for creating single-factorial models, describing the influence of each factor on $\hat{y}$ (controlling $\hat{y}$ for one variable factor);
10. Effect of each factor on $\hat{y}$ (estimation of factor's role x_i).

Example 2.7. Solve the main problems, appearing in analysis of a polynomial model.
Given:
regression equation of concrete strength (R_{cmp}, MPa):

$$\hat{y} = 57{,}3 - 1{,}6\,x_1 + 22{,}9\,x_2 + 7{,}2\,x_3 - 1{,}6\,x_4 - 0{,}4\,x_1^2 - 1{,}6\,x_2^2 -$$
$$- 0{,}4\,x_3^2 - 2{,}8\,x_4^2 - 1{,}4\,x_1 x_2 + 2{,}5\,x_2 x_3 \qquad (2.88)$$

Planning conditions are presented in Table 2.33.

Table 2.33. Conditions of experiment's planning

Factors		Variation levels			Variation interval
Natural form*	Coded form	-1	0	+1	
W, kg /m^3	x_1	160	190	220	30
C/W	x_2	1.5	2.5	3.5	1
R$_{cem}$, MPa	x_3	49.4	58.75	68.1	9.35
Ad, % of cement mass (for a dry mixture)	x_4	0	0.25	0.5	0.25

* W - water content, C/W – cement-water ratio, R$_{cem}$ – cement ultimate strength, Ad – admixture content.

1. Interpolation problem. Solving interpolation problems allows finding the output parameter's value in the factor's variation domain from +1 to -1. Substituting the coded value of each factor into the obtained regression equation (for example, 0.25, 0.5, 0.75, -0.3, -0.6, -0.75), the value of the output parameter is obtained for any intermediate factors' combinations.

Example 2.7-a. Calculate the output parameter's value due to a change in factor x_2 - cement-water ratio (Table 2.34). Other factors are assumed to be at the zero level: W=190 kg/m^3, R$_{cem}$=58.75 MPa, Ad=0.25%.

The regression equation (2.88) takes the form:

$$\hat{y} = 57.3 + 22.9\, x_2 - 1.6\, x_2^2 . \tag{2.89}$$

Table 2.34. Interpolation results following Eq. (2.89)

x_2 (coded form)	-0,8	-0,6	-0,5	-0,4	-0,2	0,2	0,4	0,5	0,6	0,8
C/W (natural form)	1,7	1,9	2,0	2,1	2,3	2,7	2,9	3,0	3,1	3,3
R$_{cmp}$, MPa	38,0	43,0	45,5	47,9	52,7	61,8	66,2	68,4	70,5	74,6

2. Extrapolation problem. Solving extrapolation problems enables predicting the output parameter's value out the factor's variation domain, for example, for x_j=1.1, 1.2, 1.3. However, it should be kept in mind that extrapolation yields certain prediction errors, becoming lower as the predicted value falls closer to the variation domain. Extrapolation is possible if the researcher has no doubt that outside the factor's variation domain, the dependence nature is the same.

Example 2.7-b. Solution of the extrapolation problem for the same conditions following Eq. (2.88) is given in Table 2.35.

Table 2.35. Extrapolation results following Eq. (2.88)

x_2 (coded form)	-1,3	-1,2	-1,1	1,1	1,2	1,3
C/W (natural form)	1,2	1,3	1,4	3,6	3,7	3,8
R_{cmp}, MPa	24,8	27,5	30,2	80,6	82,5	84,4

3. *Analytical-geometrical problem.* Solving analytical-geometrical problems enables creating graphs and nomograms for obtaining values of the output parameter within the factor's variation domain, based on the regression equations. It allows quick setting of the output parameter due to changes in each factor.

Example 2.7-c. The response surface for strength vs. factors C/W (x_2) and R_{cem} (x_3) is shown in Fig. 2.14. Other factors were assumed at zero level: W=190 kg/m^3, Ad=0.25%. The regression equation (2.88) takes the form:

$$\hat{y} = 57.3 + 22.9\,x_2 + 7.2\,x_3 - 1.6\,x_2^2 - 0.4\,x_3^2 + 2.5\,x_2 x_3 . \qquad (2.90)$$

The response surface (Figure 2.14) shows isolines of identical strength values. The coordinates of the isolines are calculated by Eq. (2.87).

4. *Optimization problems* are aimed at finding a combination of factors that maximize (or minimize) the output parameter's value or the efficiency criterion for given constraints.

In such case, the extremum is found by consequent differentiating the equation for $x_1, x_2, \ldots, x_j$. The obtained system of linear equations is equaled to zero. Solving this system, the values of x_i, yielding the extreme value of $\hat{y}$, are found. Substituting the obtained values of x_i into the initial equation, the extremum of the output parameter is found. For example, to find the combination of factors, providing the extreme value ŷ, regression equation is differentiated by x_1, x_2, x_3:

$$\hat{y} = b_0 + b_1x_1 + b_2x_2 + b_3x_3 + b_{11}x_1^2 + b_{22}x_2^2 + b_{33}x_3^2 + b_{12}x_1 x_2 +$$

$$+b_{13}x_1 x_3 + b_{23} x_2 x_3 \tag{2.91}$$

It results in:

$$\frac{dy}{dx_1} = b_1 + 2b_{11} x_1 + b_{12} x_2 + b_{13} x_3 = 0 \tag{2.92}$$

$$\frac{dy}{dx_2} = b_2 + 2b_{22} x_2 + b_{12} x_1 + b_{23} x_3 = 0 \tag{2.93}$$

$$\frac{dy}{dx_3} = b_3 + 2b_{33} x_3 + b_{13} x_1 + b_{23} x_2 = 0 \tag{2.94}$$

Using appropriate transformations, Eqs. (2.92-2.94) are represented as three linear equations that can be solved by substitution or other known methods.

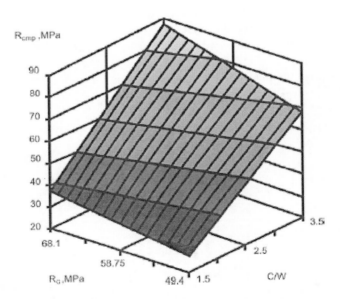

Figure 2.14. Response surface for concrete strength, following Eq. (2.90).

Example 2.7-d. It is required to find the maximum and minimum concrete strengths using Eq. (2.88).

Differentiate the regression equation (2.88), equate the partial derivatives to zero and analyze the output parameter value on the border of the factor's variation domain.

$$\frac{d\hat{y}}{dx_1} = -1.6 - 0.8\,x_1 - 1.4\,x_2 = 0$$

$$\frac{d\hat{y}}{dx_2} = 22.9 - 3.2\,x_2 - 1.4\,x_1 + 2.5\,õ_3 = 0$$

$$\frac{d\hat{y}}{dx_3} = 7.2 - 0.8\,x_3 + 2.5\,x_2 = 0 \qquad\qquad (2.95)$$

$$\frac{d\hat{y}}{dx_4} = -1.6 - 5.6\,x_4 = 0$$

Solving the obtained system (2.95) using, for example, the Gauss method, yields x_1=9.94, x_2=-6.82, x_3=-12.33, x_4=-0.29, i.e., the extremum point is outside the variation domain. Therefore, it is expedient to determine the function on the border of the variation domain.

A simple analysis of the regression equation (2.88) enables concluding that it reaches the maximum value for x_1=-1, x_2=x_3=1 and x_4 close to zero, and the minimum value is obtained for x_1= x_4=1, x_2=x_3=-1. (Table 2.36 shows the concrete strength values in some specific points (in general, it is required to scan all values on the boundary)).

Table 2.36. Concrete strength in selected specific points

Factors (coded form)				Concrete strength ($\hat{y}$), MPa
x_1	x_2	x_3	x_4	
-1	1	1	1	86.1
-1	1	1	0	90.5
-1	1	1	-0.29	90.7
-1	1	1	1	86.1
1	-1	-1	-1	25.9
1	-1	-1	0	27.1
1	-1	-1	1	22.7

Thus, the highest strength value of 90,7 MPa is obtained for $x_1=-1$, $x_2=x_3=1$, $x_4=0.29$, and the lowest is 22.7 MPa that was obtained for $x_1=x_4=1$, $x_2=x_3=-1$.

5. *Problems of output parameter control.* A general control problem is to identify a combination of factors providing the given output parameters. With this aim, the most significant factor in the regression equation (for example, concrete strength) is selected (usually C/W). Solving the regression equation for this factor, its required value, providing output parameter's value, is found when other factors are changed.

Control for a fixed $\hat{y}$ may be performed using isolines for two independent factors x_i or nomograms—for all factors.

Example 2.7-e. For drawing isolines for factors x_2 and x_3 in Eq. (2.88), let $x_1=x_4=0$. Then

$$\hat{y} = 57.3 + 22.9\,x_2 + 7.2\,x_3 - 1.6\,x_2^2 - 0.4\,x_3^2 + 2.5\,x_2 x_3 \qquad (2.96)$$

Assuming possible values of $\hat{y}$, the equation is represented in a form of $x_3=f(x_2)$, and the isolines are found.

Following Figure 2.15, for example, to get concrete strength of 60 MPa using cement with $R_{cem}=50$ MPa, the C/W should be 3.0, and for cement with $R_{cem}=60$ MPa C/W=2.58. The other factors are W=190 kg/m^3, Ad=0.25%.

Using nomograms is discussed below.

6. *Minimization problems.* A typical minimization problem is to obtain such factor's combination that yields the desired output parameters by a minimum value of one of the factors, e.g., the cement content C.

Example 2.7-f. For a given model (Eq. 2.88) the main resource, defining the cost of concrete, is cement content, which is proportional to C/W. Hence, minimal C/W will correspond to minimal resources expenditure. For example, for concrete with compressive strength of 40 Mpa, the minimum cement content is obtained for C/W=1,6. In this case $R_{cem}=68.1$ MPa, W=190 kg/m^3, Ad=0,25%.

7. *Visual representation of the studied response function's geometric image* can be obtained creating a corresponding geometric surface in two- or three-dimensional space. With this aim, a second order equation is converted into a typical canonical form.

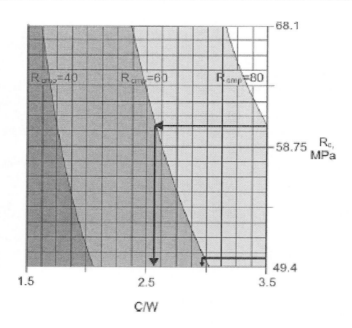

Figure 2.15. Strength isolines according to Eq. (2.96).

The process of transforming the second-order model to canonical form is divided into two stages: 1) rotating the coordinate axes and their co-location with the eigenvectors' directions (the new coordinate axes are called canonical), and 2) transferring the origin to a particular point.

The first phase allows exclusion of factor's interaction from the equation and the second minimizes the number of linear members. Such transformations are widely described in analytic geometry guidelines. Second-order surfaces, transformed to canonical form, can be classified depending on the mathematical structure of the equation.

8. Compromise problems. In solving extremum problems, related to the studying concrete properties and technology, in most cases, simultaneous multi-parameter optimization should be considered. In such cases, compromise problems are solved. A compromise between several optimization parameters is found, because a conditional extremum for one response surface is constrained by one or more other response surfaces.

For optimization of concrete composition, it is usually necessary to solve extremum problems, considering multiple optimization criteria (mechanical, deformation and special material properties). Very often, searching the response surface conditional extremum requires consideration of economic constraints.

To solve compromise extreme problems, graphical or analytical methods are used. Graphical technique for solving compromise problems is based on examining combined two-dimensional cross-sections of the response surfaces and visual choose of appropriate conditional extremes.

For analytical method of compromise problems' solving, the undetermined Lagrange multipliers can be used. The method is based on using undetermined multipliers to find the extreme values of functions, governed by some relations. The disadvantage of the undetermined Lagrange multipliers method is that it is effective only for joint consideration of two optimization criteria, and additionally, it is quite complex.

9. Effect of individual factors. For graphical interpretation of individual factor's impact and assessing their degree of influence, single-valued models and graphs are created. These models enable determining the influence degree of each factor.

Example 2.7-g. Calculate the influence degree of the individual factors involved in the polynomial model (2.88). Calculations results are given in Figure 2.16 and Table 2.37.

Analysis of the obtained data shows that the factors can be grouped by their influence degree in the following sequence: $x_2 > x_3 > x_4 > x_1$.

Increase of x_2 and x_3 yields a growth of $\hat{y}$, and increase of x_1 yields a decrease of $\hat{y}$. Increase of x_4 from 0 to 0.18% yields higher strength, but further growth of x_4 decreases the strength if other factors are constant.

Table 2.37. Calculations results for partial equations and extremum values according to Eq. (2.88)

Investigated factor		Single-factorial model*	Value of $\hat{y}$, MPa		$\Delta\hat{y}$
Natural form	Coded form		min.	max.	
W,kg/m^3	x_1	$\hat{y} = 57.3 - 1.6\,x_1 - 0.4\,x_1^2$	55.3	58.5	3.2
C/W	x_2	$\hat{y} = 57.3 + 22.9\,x_2 - 1.6\,x_2^2$	32.8	78.6	45.8
R$_{cem}$, MPa	x_3	$\hat{y} = 57.3 + 7.2\,x_3 - 0.4\,x_3^2$	49.7	64.1	14.4
Ad,% of cement mass	x_4	$\hat{y} = 57.3 - 1.6\,x_4 - 2.8\,x_4^2$	52.9	57.5	5.4

* Other factors were assumed at zero level.

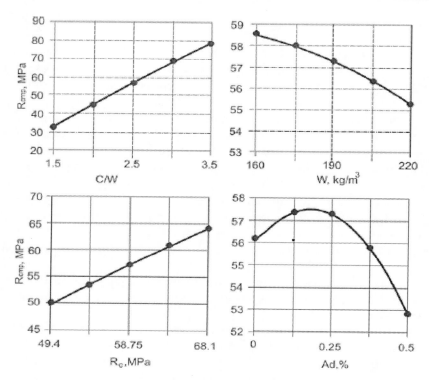

Figure 2.16. Examples of single-factorial dependences according to Eq. (2.88)

Chapter 3

THE MAIN TASKS AND ALGORITHMS FOR CONCRETE COMPOSITIONS DESIGN

3.1. GENERAL INFORMATION

Design of concrete composition is a key technological problem. Its solution defines the level of operational reliability of buildings and structures, and a degree of rational resources use for their manufacturing and construction.

D. Abrams has developed a practical methodology for design concrete composition design. He has generalized results of extensive experimental researches performed at Portland Cement Association Laboratory in Chicago and formulated the primary goals of concrete compositions design and methods of their solution. Following D. Abrams, the goal of concrete composition design is *"choice of a water-cement factor, corresponding to given strength and operating conditions of constructions, and finding of such aggregates' combination that yields the required quality and suitable consistence of concrete mix."* Additionally, the cost of concrete production and placement should be minimized.

The problems of concrete composition design that were formulated at the early beginning of concrete technologies remains actual in the present time, too. In modern technology, design of concrete composition means justification and selecting the type of initial materials and their contents, providing the normative concrete mix requirements and hardened concrete properties for a given optimization criterion. Using the system approach methodology for concrete composition design may include a number of additional problems, associated with technological parameters' and design requirements' optimization. D. Abrams suggested for the first time two methods for concrete composition design: so-called "Test method" or experimental proportioning method and method of preliminary calculations. Practice has shown that both methods are useful.

Recent developments in concrete science, computerization of technological and technical-economic calculations have offered new opportunities for development of computational concrete composition design method. Calculated concrete mixes compositions require experimental verification prior to industrial use. However, the calculation method application is especially useful when it is necessary to estimate the resources' requirements and effectiveness of initial materials, as well as for reducing the laboratory work complexity.

D. Abrams has suggested that the above-mentioned two methods for concrete composition design should be based on a water-cement ratio rule. Further researches have shown that D. Abrams' statement that concrete strength for given materials and their processing conditions is defined just by the ratio between water and cement contents is some exaggeration, and "just" should be replaced by "mainly." A number of studies show that along with W/C, characterizing the cement glue quality, essential influence on strength of heavy concrete has its volumetric concentration and other factors.

Presently in technological practice, concrete compositions design is carried out using numerous methods, based on various theoretical and technological preconditions. All of these methods can be successfully used in practice if they solve the required tasks. As time has shown, trying to make the concrete composition design methodology more universal and discussion about preferring one of the approaches relative to others have appeared not constructive.

Actual directions for developing the methodology of concrete compositions design are:

- increasing the "forecasting ability" of design procedures, i.e., possibilities of more accurate taking into account of concrete technology factors and design requirements;
- improving the design algorithms' efficiency, their accuracy and speed.

Progress in these directions can be achieved by realizing modern concepts in concrete science regarding formation of constructive and technical properties of concrete, combined with system analysis.

The most common approach to concrete compositions design is based on quantitative account of "property-structure-concrete composition" relations by analyzing and simultaneous solution of the equations relating concrete properties parameters with those of its structure.

As a basis for such approach can be considered the following concrete science statements:

1. Most of concrete properties are functions of its structure. Depending on the character of those or other properties, the last can be mainly formed by macro- or micro-structural features of concrete. The influence of concrete structure on properties of concrete predetermines the relation between various properties.

2. Each of concrete properties is definitely related with appropriate parameters or criteria of concrete structure that considers qualitative and quantitative features of its solid phase and porous space. As concrete is a typical composite material, its structural parameters consider the features of its matrix (cement stone) and aggregates as well as their interaction.

3. Changes in various concrete properties due to varying the structural parameters and composition factors can have same or different directions. Design of concrete composition with given properties requires taking into account their orientation and in many cases, it is a compromise problem.

The optimum concrete structure provides a complex of required performance properties and satisfies the given optimality conditions (minimal expense of cement, minimal concrete mixture cost, etc.). According to this condition, concrete compositions can essentially differ for various optimality conditions.

In construction and technological practice, the most popular are methods of concrete compositions design aimed at receiving the required compression strength of hardened concrete. It is first of all because concrete strength is its basic parameter for structural design. Another reason is the assumption that other concrete properties are also definitely related with strength. This assumption, however, is not common enough. Really, concrete compressive, flexural and tensile strengths as well as its wear and cavitational resistance, etc., are definitely interdependent. However, dependence between strength and frost resistance, strength and creep, etc., are not definite; their determination should be based on using a complex of special quantitative dependences.

3.2. The Main Tasks in Design of Concrete Compositions

Design of concrete compositions may be considered as an independent system (first class of problems) and as a subsystem of more general technological systems, such as design of concrete and reinforced concrete structures and their technology (second class of problems). In the first case, the problem is to obtain an optimal concrete composition, providing the required parameters, and in the second case, these parameters (mixture workability, concrete strength, etc.) are additionally optimized.

According to current practice, mainly the first class problems are solved, which is not always sufficient. For example, manufacturers try to achieve maximum saving in cement for producing concrete with given strength, but it is not effective, in cases when the strength is not an optimization parameter from the structures' cost viewpoint. In particular, the use of high-strength concrete may allow reduction of the reinforced concrete elements' cross-sections. Thus, cement content per unit product (element) may be more effective than that per cubic meter of concrete. Similarly, the concrete mix workability that significantly affects the concrete composition is also not always economically feasible. For example, if the optimization criterion is the cost of the structure, using stiff concrete mixtures may be less advantageous from the manpower required for concrete compacting, compared to the cases when mixes with high slump are used, although the last ones can contain more cement. In this regard, it seems more rational to combine the efforts of designers, technology engineers and economists for a complex design of concrete, considering constructive, technological and economical aspects.

In concrete composition design for the second class of problems, multivariance is considered. Choice of a certain concrete composition is defined in definite conditions, based on the selected optimization criterion. As an optimization criterion, the following parameters can be selected: minimum cement content, minimum average concrete density, minimum concrete cost and so on. More complex criteria are the cost of the structure or even that of the entire building, taking into account not only the price of concrete but also the costs of manpower, elements' production, transportation and construction.

In the second class of problems, composition parameters (aggregates ratio, admixtures content, etc.) as well as technological and structural parameters can be chosen as optimized factors of concrete mixtures composition.

The tasks of the first problems class can be divided into one-, two- and multi-parametric. A basis of this division is based on the total number of output parameters for the concrete mixture and hardened concrete.

For one-parametric tasks, the mixture workability is usually not defined in strict quantitative limits and just its qualitative characteristic is given (semi-dry, moist or wet). Some indices of hardened concrete (concrete frost resistance, water impermeability, resistance to sulphates, etc.) can be characterized qualitatively, too. In certain cases, the method of products manufacture, concreting methods or operating conditions of structures are defined. If it is possible, the technology engineer adds to a concrete composition design problem quantitative data adequate to qualitative assessment, and the one-parameter design task is transformed into two- or multi-parametric one. In other cases, to design a composition, providing required properties, it is necessary to add restrictions regarding the water content, water-cement ratio (W/C), size and type of aggregates, admixtires' content, etc.

The most developed and implemented in practice are two-parametric tasks, in which the given concrete characteristic is its compressive strength (R_{cmp}), and for concrete mixtures, its stiffness (Vebe time) Vb or slump of Abrams cone Sl. To solve the tasks of this type, design-experimental methods are widely used. These methods are based on a number of known technological dependencies: concrete strength vs. cement-water ratio, a water content constancy rule *, an optimal sand content rule **, etc.[1]

In solving such problems for heavy concretes, the water-cement ratio, water content taking into account the desired concrete mixture workability and aggregates consumption are obtained, assuming that the concrete mix consists of all its components' absolute volumes.

In the simplest case for a four-component mixture, knowledge of three parameters is required: cement-water ratio (C/W), water content (W), an a factor, characterizing the ratio between the aggregates (sand portion in the aggregates mixture (r) or coefficient, characterizing separating of large aggregates grains' by cement -sand mortar). The last one can be considered as optimizing, because minimum cement content can be achieved just an optimal value of this factor, when C/W = const. An optimum aggregates ratio is often taken one that ensures the best workability or minimum water consumption.

---

* Water content constancy rule. According to experimental data, water content of concrete mixes with cement content of 200...400 kg/m3 and constant workability remains constant.
** Optimal sand content rule. The water content of a uniform concrete mix is minimal for a certain portion of sand in the mixture of aggregates.

Search for the optimum aggregates ratio for concrete mixtures with many components becomes a very complex task requiring application of nonlinear programming and other complicated techniques. In some cases, the problem can be simplified using empirical dependencies.

Admixtures' content may also serve as optimizing factor. For example, optimizing the added plasticizers quantity can yield minimum cement content, depending on the desired concrete mix workability and hardened concrete strength.

If it is necessary to achieve some other building and technical properties, in addition to compressive strength, the task of concrete compositions design becomes significantly more complicated.

Design of special concrete types compositions (especially for hydro-technical engineering, road construction, corrosion resistant, etc.) is a multi-parametric task. Such tasks can be divided into three subgroups:

- with normed parameters that are directly related to concrete compressive strength;
- with normed parameters that are indirectly related to concrete compressive strength;
- with normed parameters that are not related to concrete compressive strength.

The first subgroup includes, for example, problems with various normative concrete strength parameters. For design of such concrete compositions, first of all, a dominant parameter is selected from the normative concrete properties, corresponding to this parameter compression strength is found and minimal possible C/W, providing all set of properties, is obtained. The dominant parameter is such normative parameter, which achievement assumes at the same time achievement of all other parameters specified in the task conditions.

For example, from Figure 3.1 it follows that if the normative compressive strength $R_{cmp} \geq 20$ MPa, tensile flexural strength $R_{fl} \geq 8.3$ MPa and tensile splitting strength $R_{spl} \geq 7.9$ MPa, then it is evident that a dominant parameter is R_{spl} and the required C/W, providing all three properties, is 2.1.

A basic feature of such problems is existence of area C/W within the limits of which is located the C/W, providing all normative parameters. As this area becomes more narrow (for the considered example, following Figure 3.1, the area of C/W is 1.3 ... 2.1), the concrete composition is closer to optimal and cement content C → min more close. For achieving this condition, different technological methods are used: adding admixtures, regulating the concrete mixture properties, changing curing conditions, selecting initial materials, etc.

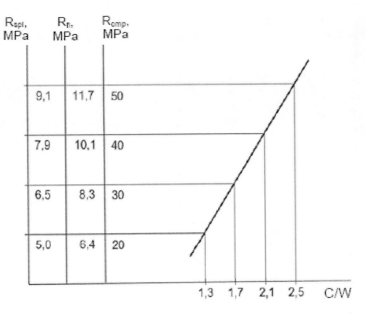

Figure 3.1. Relation between C/W and compressive (R_{cmp}), tensile flexural (R_{fl}) and splitting strength (R_{spl}) of concrete.

Normative parameters in the second subgroup problems, along with compression strength include creep, frost resistance, thermal emission, etc.

Figure 3.2 shows an example for relation between creep and cement stone content in concrete for constant R_{cmp}. The concrete creep measure (Cr) was obtained according to equation, proposed by European Concrete Commission:

$$Cr_{(28)} \frac{k \cdot W / C (W + 0.33 C)}{\sqrt{10 R_{cmp}}} \tag{3.1}$$

where k is a coefficient, depending on dimensions of the element's section (r) and humidity of the surrounding environment (θ); W and C are water and cement contents, respectively, in kg/m^3. For example, for r = 2.5 cm, θ = 70%, coefficient $k = 0.92\,10^{-6}$.

From Eq. (3.1) and Figure 3.2, it follows that for constant W/C and corresponding concrete strength the creep value can be different, depending on the content of cement stone in concrete. It can be shown in a similar way that relation between concrete strength with a group of properties, defined mainly by capillary porosity of concrete (water absorption, frost resistance, etc.) is ambiguous.

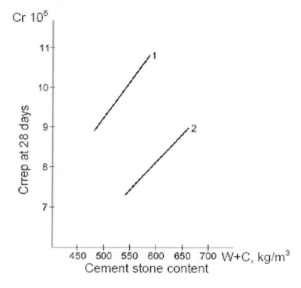

Figure 3.2. Influence of cement stone content in concrete on creep measure: 1 – R$_{cmp}$= 20 MPa; 2 – R$_{cmp}$ = 30 MPa.

Capillary porosity of concrete can be calculated using the following formula:

$$P_k = \frac{W - w_c\alpha\,C}{1000} \qquad (3.2)$$

where w_c is the content of chemically connected water (0.47...0.52), and α is the cement hydration degree. Decreasing the W/C and increasing the connected water content decreases the capillary porosity, but increasing the cement content yields an increase of the cement stone volume in concrete and consequently increases the capillary porosity.

Figure 3.3 presents a nomogram of capillary porosity of concrete according to G.I. Gorchakov. The lines of the constant porosity for $P_k > 0$ don't correspond to constant W/C and, consequently to constant concrete strength, too.

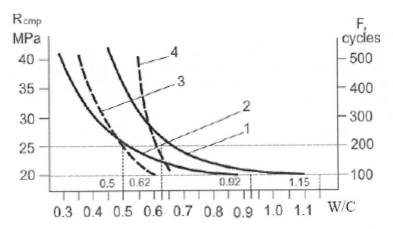

Figure 3.4. Dependence of W/C on given concrete strength and frost-resistance values: 1 – R_{cmp} without entrained air; 2 – with 20 liters of entrained air (the concrete strength is obtained for cement strength $R_c = 50$ MPa); 3 –frost resistance without entrained air; 4 – with 20 liters of entraine air.

The normative parameters in multi-parametric tasks can be formed under influence the same or essentially differing technological factors. In the above-stated example, the compressive strength and creep are defined first of all by the water-cement ratio. In a similar way, the water-cement ratio is the basic influencing factor if strength and frost resistance are the normative parameters (especially if air entraining admixtures are not used). However, unlike the first subgroup tasks, here, normative parameters are related less strictly.

For solving the tasks of this and previous subgroups, the W/C area, providing the normative parameters, is established and technological ways for narrowing this area are considered, and then final value of the normative W/C is obtained. Regulation of the normative W/C in these tasks is possible just by variation of other composition factors, like quantities of the cement paste, volume of entrained air, etc.

Example. The average concrete strength R_{cmp} = 65MPa and creep $Cr \times 10^6$ = 3.5are normalized. The concrete mix includes crushed granite stone and medium-grained quartz sand, and the cone slump equals 2 cm. The cement ultimate strength is R_c=50MPa. Following the formula for concrete strength, $R_{cmp} = AR_c(C/W - 0.5)$ for A=0.6 W/C=0.38. For water content W=175 l/m^3 and corresponding cement content C = 460 kg/m^3, the creep measure is not provided ($Cr \times 10^6$ = 4.5). For achieving the normative value of $Cr \times 10^6$, the W/C value should be decreased. The same value of W/C from strength and creep conditions can be achieved practically by using a more stiff mixture.

A powerful tool of "scissors" reduction by W/C in frost-resistant concrete is entrained air. It is common in this case that significantly increasing W/C for achievement of required frost resistance, the entrained air at the same time reduces the necessary W/C ratio from strength condition. Thus, the general positive effect of cement expense reduction may be quite considerable, especially in concrete with high frost resistance values at moderate normalized strength value.

From Figure3.4, for example, it follows that R_{cmp} = 20 MPa and F200 (cycles of freezing and thawing) are provided without entrained air for W/C=0.5, and with entrained air W/C=0.62. Thus the "scissors" size by W/C is 0.31 and 0.1 in the first and second cases, respectively.

In a similar way, the water content "scissors" are formed, for example, by concrete mix workability and concrete shrinkage (Figure 3.5).

It requires including special calculations in algorithms of multi-parametric tasks of concrete composition design. These calculations are related to obtaining compositions that provide the entire complex of normalized properties.

Decreasing the intervals of the required composition parameters and moving them to the side, providing minimal possible cement content, is a concrete composition optimization task.

For some concrete compositions design tasks (for example, for light concretes), W/C is not a dominant factor, providing a complex of normalized properties.

For such tasks, it is necessary to find another factor that would be essential for all normalized properties. Finding the necessary value of this factor becomes the main task of concrete composition design.

Development of general and convenient calculation-experimental method for design of concrete mixtures with given workability and concrete strength became possible due to some assumptions, based on physical rules, caused by the influence of concrete structure on its properties.

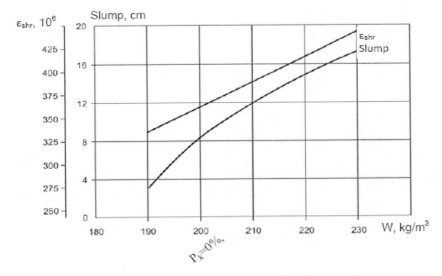

Figure 3.5. Influence of water content on concrete mix slump and shrinkage.

These rules can be used in multi-parametrical concrete compositions design, too. Thus the general sketch of the method is:

1. Taking into account the design requirements to concrete, technological conditions, technical and economic analysis, the initial components of a concrete mixture and its workability are selected.

2. When concrete properties, directly related with concrete compression strength R_{cmp} (tensile, flexural strengths, module of elasticity, etc.) are normalized, the value of R_{cmp}, providing the given properties, is calculated.

3. Taking into account the ultimate cement strength, qualitative features of aggregates, curing conditions and other factors, the C/W, providing the required properties, is calculated.

4. For achieving the required workability parameter and if necessary other concrete mixture and concrete properties (for example, shrinkage), water content W for the given initial materials and additives is obtained. In case of exceeding the water constancy rule limits, the water content is corrected considering C/W.

5. If the concrete frost resistance is normalized, the required volume emulsified air is calculated, and the C/W ratio is corrected.

6. For the obtained values of W and C/W, the possibility of achieving the normalized properties, defined by these two technological parameters, is checked. If the normalized parameters are not provided, W and C/W are further adjusted using, if it is necessary, special techniques (adding admixtures, etc.).

7. Using the obtained C/W and W, the cement content is found and restrictions regarding the cement consumption (heat evolution, corrosion resistance, etc.) are verified.

8. Composition of fine and coarse aggregate with several factions, and then their content is calculated. The aggregates' ratio is chosen taking into account achieving the best workability and strength as well as other conditions (high water resistance, structural elements thickness, reinforcement degree, etc.).

9. Possibility of using different technological solutions, aimed at saving cement, reducing energy consumption, minimizing the concrete mixture cost, are considered.

3.3. QUALITATIVE DEPENDENCES BETWEEN PROPERTIES, HARDENING REGIME AND CONCRETE COMPOSITION

Solving concrete compositions design problems using mathematical experiment planning includes obtaining relationships between the basic concrete mix and hardened concrete properties and factors that affect them.

At a priori study of the relationships that define the concrete properties and their qualitative structure for further mathematical modeling and optimization, it is important to select the main controlled factors and to evaluate the possible curvature of the response surface in the variation region. Relatively high information level regarding the influence of composition factors and hardening regime on the basic concrete properties allows, in most cases, performing qualitative analysis and modeling almost immediately in the stationary region, which greatly simplifies the optimum search.

Based on numerous studies, it is possible to define three main groups of factors involved in concrete properties formation: 1) qualitative parameters of the initial components, 2) quantitative parameters of the mixture, 3) regime parameters of hardening processes.

It is impossible to consider all factors in traditional and in system-optimization approaches, although the last one has more relevant opportunities. At the first stage, depending on the task, correct regulated factors should be chosen and the most important of them for the given output parameters should be selected. Rest of the factors should be fixed and unregulated, but influential factors should be also considered. Some technological factors may correlate each with other. In this case, analysis of their joint impact on output parameters of the system is irrelevant.

When optimizing the mix compositions, providing the complex of typical concrete output parameters, the most important factors of the first group are mineralogical and chemical composition of cements and admixtures, their dispersion, structural and mineralogical peculiarities and aggregates' fineness; the second group is water consumption and water-cement ratio, the ratio between aggregates and admixtures content; the third group is hardening duration and temperature.

Chemical and mineralogical composition of cement as well as its fineness affect its integral indexes-strength and cement paste normal consistency. However, there are no strict general quantitative dependences between these parameters because the mechanism of forming the structure of cement paste and stone is complicated. Statistical relationships can only be set for each specific cement plant. Different chemical and mineralogical compositions of cements with same strength have different influence on concrete properties, especially strength after heat treatment, frost resistance, corrosion resistance and so on. According to modern results, the content of tricalcium aluminate as well as the ratio between the aluminate and alite phases in cement more significantly affect these properties. According to our data, a general dependence between concrete strength and the cement strength has an exponential form, while the exponent decreases and becomes closer to one as the overall curing duration is longer.

Influence of cement paste normal consistency affects primarily the water content of the concrete mixture and, consequently, all the major concrete properties. Cement paste normal consistency is closely related to content of mineral admixtures in cement.

Addition of plasticizers and air-entraining surface-active substances (SAS) is a common practice in concrete technology. Their influence on concrete properties is well studied. In search of optimal concrete mixtures composition, it is important to take into account the extreme influence of SAS on concrete properties at constant workability. Location and size of the extremum in the property- SAS concentration coordinates depends on the type of admixtures, levels of other factors and the required workability value. Thus, the effect of air-entraining admixtures on frost resistance of concrete is higher for concrete from moist mixes than stiff ones. Effect of such plasticizers as technical lignosulphonates, which are mainly acting not by additional air-entraining but by peptization of cement paste, is higher in mixtures with comparatively enlarged cement content. Addition of complex SAS is more universal.

When concrete is subjected to heat treatment, the effect of SAS admixtures is different and depends on the nature, air-entraining ability, composition of the mixture and the combination of regime parameters. Most researchers report that adding optimum concentration of SAS can be effective at moderate and extended regimes with pre-exposure. SAS effectiveness at heat treatment increases with addition of hardening accelerators to cement or concrete mixture.

In the second group of factors, the most important are water content in concrete mixture and water-cement ratio. Water content and water-cement ratio characterize the quality and quantity of cement paste and consequently the cement stone in concrete. Properties of concrete mix and hardened concrete are in different ways related to those two factors. Water content has a dominant influence on concrete mixes' workability, and the effect of W/C is evident just after a certain threshold; for hardened concrete, the water-cement ratio has a principal influence on the strength properties at the entire range.

On frost resistance and water impermeability of concrete along with water-cement ratio significantly affects the initial water content of the mixture. Due to developing destructive processes, the influence of water content on strength and other properties of concrete is essential for forced thermal processing conditions.

Effect of qualitative and quantitative parameters of cement-water system on the concrete mix and hardened concrete should be considered together. It is known, for example, that the lower the cement stone density, the higher should be its content to provide the necessary concrete strength, frost resistance and water impermeability. However, there is some optimum quantity of cement stone at constant quality parameters, and exceeding this value yields no noticeable effect on concrete strength and other properties. This concept is closely related to modern ideas regarding the concrete structure.

Additionally, there are many other technological factors having a significant impact on the concrete properties. Among them, first of all, should be mentioned most of the aggregates' parameters (mineralogy, fineness (coarseness), shape, grain composition, strength, water absorption, adhesive properties) and relation between them. Of particular interest in terms of concrete composition optimization are well-regulated factors such as fineness, grain composition and the aggregates ratio.

The role of grain composition and aggregates ratio in the formation of concrete properties is studied sufficiently. It was reported that for concrete mixture with constant water content, the impact of sand particles in the aggregates' mix on workability has an extreme nature. In a common case, the best aggregates' ratio should provide minimum water content and, consequently, minimum cement consumption yielding the necessary properties and preventing the concrete mixture separation. Optimal sand quantity changes by varying the cement paste content, water-cement ratio and air volume, involved in concrete mix.

In the third group of technological factors, hardening duration has the major influence on the concrete properties. If heat treatment is used additionally to the overall process duration, then the ratio between the preliminary exposure, isothermal heating duration, temperature rise rate and cooling have significant influence. Affect of hardening regime parameters on the concrete properties is closely related to the properties of initial materials and mixture composition. According to modern knowledge, the overall hardening duration and relation between steaming regime parameters, as well as binders' expenditure required to get the concrete with the same strength, depends on cement type, its chemical and mineralogical composition. The main destructive processes occur in concrete during increasing and decreasing the temperature, whereas the concrete strength grows during isothermal heating. Hence, proper using all regime parameters of the process is important. It is known that the optimal duration of preliminary exposure can range from two to eight hours and more. It is recommended to be reduced as the cement strength and ambient temperature increase, W/C reduces, the rate of temperature rise decreases, or in cases when accelerators of hardening are used, complex profile products are steamed, etc. Similarly, complex interactions with other technological factors should be considered for selecting optimum heating rate, duration and temperature of isothermal treatment.

Thus, brief analysis of a priori information regarding the regularities of "property–hardening regime–concrete composition" enables drawing the following conclusions for mathematical modeling:

1) technological factors affect the properties of concrete complexly, interacting with each other;
2) the impact of most factors is non-linear in a relatively wide range, so for mathematical description of the basic concrete mix and hardened concrete properties, in most cases second-order polynomial equations should be used.

3.4. USING MATHEMATICAL MODELS FOR CONCRETE COMPOSITIONS DESIGN

The first works related to application of mathematical modeling in concrete technology using factorial planning of experiment were already aimed at solving problems of concrete mixture compositions design. The optimization problem of dry aggregates grain composition was first solved using linear programming methods and then by applying second-order rotatable planning. Later, simplex-grade plans were proposed for optimizing ratio of different fractions in the aggregates' mixture and investigating the concrete strength dependence on aggregates' content. These plans were further used for solving other problems, like finding the optimum composition of admixtures, predicting the concrete frost resistance, etc. Simplex planning was also used for design of some types of concrete and other multi-component compositions. However, in these works, the optimization problem was reduced to finding the components ratio providing the necessary combination of material properties. Minimization of some component's consumption, for example cement content, was not the goal. The components' quality factors were also not considered.

The first attempt to apply mathematical experiment planning for solving the problem of choosing the concrete mix components ratio, providing the required concrete strength and concrete mixture workability with minimal cement expenditure was made at the end of sixties of the twentieth century. E. Sorkin (Russia) proposed mathematical models for concrete mix workability (Vebe time) vs. water content, water-cement ratio, sand-crushed stone ratio, cement paste normal consistency, and also obtained a model of concrete compressive strength considering the influence of composition factors and cement strength.

Simultaneous solution of the concrete mixtures' workability and concrete strength equations enabled proposal of a new method for concrete composition design. It allows obtaining analytical and graphical dependences, following from the models of strength, W/C value, providing necessary ultimate concrete strength and taking into account cement strength, and the ratio between aggregates, providing the minimum water consumption for given concrete mixture workability, cement paste normal consistency and W/C. However, solving the problem by this method is ambiguous in terms of significant affect on the mixture's water content. The study also deals with a problem of finding the optimal concrete mix composition from materials' cost and cost per unit viewpoints. For this reason, by varying the "composition factors," appropriate regression equations were found and compromise problems were solved graphically under constraints on concrete strength and mixture workability.

This method of concrete composition design was developed also in other works. G. Mihailenko obtained quadratic models of concrete mix workability (Vebe time) in a large range. To prevent the model's inadequacy, caused by the dispersion non-homogeneity, a logarithmic transformation of response function was used. Optimization of concrete composition was proposed to be carried out by the following steps:

1. Experimental constants' evaluation in the concrete strength equation - C/W;
2. Obtaining the minimum cement-water ratio (C/W), providing the required concrete strength using the dependence $R_{cmp} = f(C/W)$;
3. Creating a model of concrete mixture's workability and curves of uniform workability in coordinates "sand portion in a mixture of aggregates (r) – water content W" for required values of C/W.
4. Finding the optimal r value, providing for a given C/ W the required concrete mixture workability and minimum water content.

This approach differs from that proposed E. Sorkin just by a way for finding the C/W ratio. Both methods assume that at constant C/W, water content and cement stone volume concentration do not affect the strength, and this significantly simplifies the optimization problem. However, this assumption is not strict for high-slump and semi-dry concrete mixtures. For concrete that hardens in forced heat treatment regimes, the assumption is unacceptable.

This problem can be solved using a graphically analytical method proposed by the authors, considering possible effects on the concrete strength simultaneously with the water-cement ratio and water content. Its essence is as follows:

1. Obtaining the quadratic model for concrete mixture workability, and solving it for water content. It allows obtaining the value of sand portion in a mixture of aggregates (r) for different cement contents, providing minimum water consumption of the concrete mix, required for a given workability.

2. Using a two-factorial plan and experiments are realized to find the dependence of concrete strength on water and cement consumptions in a form of second- and first-order polynomials (for C/W ᵹ 2.5 and C/W <2.5, respectively). For finding the concrete mixture composition at each point of the matrix, the optimum value of s_e is chosen, based on results of previous calculations, using the workability model.

3. Cement content (C) required to obtain a certain concrete strength (R_{cmp}) is obtained from a curve $R_{cmp} = f$ (C/W) for a given workability. Water content (W) and optimal sand portion in a mixture of aggregates (r_{opt}) of the concrete mix can be found for the required cement consumption from the corresponding curves, obtained by combining extreme dependence values W=f (r) for various cement consumption values.

This method allows optimization of the concrete mixture composition. In this case, however, a non-optimal algorithm, requiring a large number of calculations for graphs plotting, is used.

An improved analytical solution of the concrete mix composition optimization problem is further proposed. It is based on finding a quadratic model of concrete mixture's workability (Vebe time) Vb and concrete strength R_{cmp} depending on contents of water W and cement C as well as on sand portion in the aggregates mix r :

$$Vb = f(W, C, r) \qquad\qquad (3.3)$$

$$R_{cmp} = f(W, C, r) \qquad\qquad (3.4)$$

As the sand portion in a mixture of aggregates is the main factor that determines the minimum water consumption, and consequently the expenditure of cement with given strength and paste normal consistency, factor r is considered as an optimization parameter. This parameter takes a number of values in the variation region with a corresponding number of response surfaces. Considering the expression

$$f(W, C, r, Vb) = 0 \qquad\qquad (3.5)$$

as a family of one-parameter surfaces, the following equations system is obtained:

$$\begin{cases} f(W, C, r, Vb) = 0 \\ \partial f / \partial r = 0 \end{cases} \qquad (3.6)$$

Simultaneous solution of Eq (3.6) with the strength equation enables finding the optimal value of water and cement contents as well as the portion of sand in the mixture of aggregates for obtaining a concrete mix with required workability and hardened concrete with necessary strength.

A number of methods for concrete composition optimization were developed not only for ordinary but also for lightweight and special types of concrete. They are usually confined to finding the interpolation equations that provide relations between the output parameters and technological factors and further investigation of response surfaces using usual canonical analysis, isolines or nomograms.

Mathematical modeling allows solution of problems related to design of concrete compositions for cases with a wide variety of initial conditions and factors. However, in most works on finding optimal concrete compositions, it is used without considering other systems analysis principles. In some tasks that use modeling, there is no preliminary analysis, there is no objective background for factor's selection, indicators' choice and performance criteria, clear formulation of the optimization goal, and all the necessary constraints are not considered. It significantly reduces the optimization solutions' value and its strictness.

Optimization of concrete composition design with application of mathematical models is often proposed to be carried out graphically. In spite of appropriateness of graphical decisions, especially in complicated optimization problems, in many cases it is nevertheless preferable to use analytical and graphical-analytical methods.

Graphical interpretation is especially valuable when nomographing the results found using the analytical solutions of mathematical models. In some works, creating polynomial models can be entirely replaced by traditional approach.

For concrete, designed for multiple output parameters, such as hydraulic concrete, the composition optimization problem is especially difficult and can be strictly solved just using a system of mathematical models. The first attempt to use polynomial models to solve the problem of determining the concrete composition, providing the required concrete mix workability as well as strength, frost resistance and other properties of hardened concrete, was made in the previous works of the authors.

Despite a relatively high level of a priori information, the entire complex of relationships between the technological factors determining the efficiency of concrete compositions at different curing conditions cannot be obtained with sufficient quality and, moreover quantitatively without mathematical modeling.

Polynomial regression equations in concrete composition design tasks of can be used as conventional quantitative relationships that are valid under certain boundary conditions. If for normalized concrete properties $\sum\limits_{i=1}^{m} y_i$ were obtained squared polynomial models with $x_1, x_2...x_n...x_K$ given factors, then it is possible to obtain the value of factor x_n, for example, the cement-water ratio, by presenting the models in a form of quadratic equations:

$$b_0 + \sum_{i=1}^{K} b_i x_i + \sum_{i=1}^{K} b_{ii} x_i^2 + \sum_{i \neq j} b_{ij} x_i x_j - y_i = 0 \tag{3.7}$$

Setting the normalized parameter value (y_i) and stabilizing other factors at a certain level, it is possible to find the value of x_n as the equation root:

$$x_n = \frac{-C_n \pm \sqrt{C_n^2 - 4b_{nn} l}}{2b_{nn}} \tag{3.8}$$

where

$$C_n = b_n + \sum_{\substack{i=1 \\ i \neq n}}^{K} b_{ni} x_i$$

$$l = \sum_{\substack{i=1 \\ i \neq n}}^{K} b_i x_i + \sum_{\substack{i=1 \\ i \neq n}}^{K} b_{ii} x_i^2 + \sum_{\substack{i=1 \\ i \neq j}}^{K} b_{ij} x_i x_j - y_i$$

Finding the factor's value in natural units is achieved by transformation performed using Eq. (2.7).

Multi-factorial polynomial models enable finding the optimal values of such factors as aggregates' ratio, additives content, etc., and thus optimizing the designed concrete compositions, taking into account a given set of factors and their variation range. There are two possible approaches:

1) The optimized factors are determined from the equations, in which they are dependent variables, for example, the portion of sand in the aggregates mixture, r, is found from the slump or the concrete mix workability equation.

2) Equations for the optimized factors (r_{opt}, superplasticizer additives, etc.) are obtained and used together with the equations of normalized parameters for design of concrete mixtures composition.

Along with differential analysis, using canonical and isoparametrical analysis as well as linear programming and alternative methods for getting optimal solutions is also possible.

Table 3.1 presents examples of developed by the authors' algorithms for concrete compositions design.

Table 3.1. Examples of algorithms for solving concrete compositions optimization tasks

Problem formulation: Design compositions for concretes with compressive strength 25...35 MPa and concrete mixes workability 10...30 sec (by Vebe) using Portland cement with ultimate strength of 40 and 50 MPa.

Composition factors: water content, kg/m^3 (x_1); cement content, kg/m^3 (x_2); portion of sand in the aggregates' mixture (x_3); ultimate cement strength, MPa (x_4).

Output parameters: concrete mix stiffness, sec (y_1); concrete compressive strength, MPa (y_2).

Design scheme: 1. As a result of algorithmic experiments' realization, quadratic polynomial models y_1 and y_2 are obtained.

2. Obtain a linear equation $P_1/_C \rightarrow$ max .

3. For given values of x_4, y_1 and y_2, the required parameters of the mix x_1, x_2, x_3 are found by solving three equations.

Problem formulation: Design compositions for concrete with compressive strength 15...50 MPa and concrete mixtures workability 10...40 sec (by Vebe) and cement paste consistency of 25-29%, using Portland cement with ultimate strength 30...60 MPa.

Composition factors: water content, kg/m^3 (x_1); cement content, kg/m^3 (x_2); portion of sand in the aggregates' mixture (x_3); part of fraction 0.63-5.0 mm in sand (x_4); cement ultimate strength, MPa (x_5); cement paste consistency, % (x_6).

Output parameters: concrete mix workability, sec (y_1); concrete compressive strength, MPa (y_2).

Table 3.1. (Continued)

Design scheme: 1. Obtain quadratic polynomial models of y_1 and y_2.

2. Obtain linear equations $\partial y_1 / \partial x_3 = 0$ and $\partial y_2 / \partial x_4 = 0$.

3. Express the optimizing factors x_3 and x_4 as functions of x_1 and x_2, transform equations for y_1 and y_2.

4. For given values of x_5 and x_6, find x_1 and x_2.

5. Find x_3 and x_4 from corresponding linear equations

Problem formulation: Design compositions for hydraulic engineering concrete.

Composition factors: water content, kg/m^3 (x_1); cement content, kg/m^3 (x_2); maximal crushed stone size (x_3); content of air entraining admixture, kg/m^3 (x_4); cement paste consistency, % (x_5); ultimate cement strength (x_6); workability (x_7); duration of normal hardening (x_8).

Output parameters: entrained volume, % (y_1); concrete mix water content, kg/m^3 (y_2); optimal sand content (y_3); concrete compressive strength, MPa (y_4); frost resistance, cycles (y_5); water impermeability, MPa (y_6).

Design scheme: 1. Obtain quadratic polynomial models of $y_1 \ldots y_6$.

2. Solve models y_4, y_5, y_6 for C/W, fixing other factors at required levels, for given strength, frost resistance and water impermeability. Select the maximum C/W.

3. Find the required contents of admixtures, water and sand using y_1, y_2, y_3 models.

4. Find the final concrete composition using the previously obtained parameters.

Problem formulation: Design compositions for self-compacting slag - containing concrete.

Composition factors: crushed stone portion in the aggregates' mix (x_1); slag portion in fine aggregate (x_2); water consumption of crushed stone, % (x_3); water content of slag, % (x_4);); water consumption of sand, % (x_5); cement-water ratio (x_6).

Output parameters: water content of the concrete mix, kg/m^3 (y_1); concrete compressive strength after steaming, MPa (y_2); concrete efficiency coefficient after steaming (strength to cement content ratio) (y_3).

Design scheme: 1. Obtain quadratic polynomial models of $y_1 \ldots y_3$.

2. Obtain linear equations $\partial y_3 / \partial x_1 = 0$ и $\partial y_3 / \partial x_2 = 0$.

3. Solve a system of three equations and obtain x_1, x_2 and x_6 for given values of other factors and required y_3.

4. Using the obtained parameters, calculate the final concrete mix composition.

The advantages of polynomial models in design of concrete compositions with the different factors, varying in a certain range, are evident. However, the polynomial models locality, providing a satisfactory prediction of the response function just in strictly defined conditions and often in a very narrow varying factors range, should be taken into account. Moreover, there is a factorial barrier, complicating the task of obtaining such models for high number of factors that should be taken into account also.

It is possible to reduce these shortcomings of polynomial models in some ways for design of concrete compositions by creating standard models for concrete properties using typical materials. Such models are valid in a wide range of the most technological factors. Using computerized adaptive identification algorithms allows models adjustment if the initial conditions were changed.

The choice of strategies and methods for optimizing the concrete mixtures composition are determined by the task peculiarities.

Chapter 4 includes typical examples of solving specific problems of optimal concrete compositions design using polynomial models.

EXAMPLES OF CONCRETE COMPOSITIONS DESIGN USING MATHEMATICAL MODELLING

This chapter presents compositions design tasks examples for concretes with different kind, amount and features of initial materials, optimization terms and number of the rationed parameters. In all examples, mathematical models, obtained by the statistical processing of experimental data, are used. Solving such tasks by traditional methods usually requires considerably more time and carrying out more experiments than in case when mathematical models are used.

4.1. DESIGN OF CONCRETE COMPOSITIONS WITH GIVEN STRENGTH AND WORKABILITY VALUES

Example 4.1. It is required to design optimal compositions for concrete with ultimate compressive strength of 20...30 MPa and mix workability in a range of 10...30 sec (Vebe) using Portland cement with compressive 28 days strength of 37...53 MPa. For concrete production are used: crushed stone (fraction 5...20 mm) and quartz sand with fineness modulus $M_{fn}=2.04$.

To create models of concrete mix workability and hardened concrete compressive strength a B_4-type experiment plan was used (Table 8. Appendices).

Conditions of experiment planning are given in Table 4.1.

Table 4.1. Conditions of experiment planning

Factor		Variation levels			Variation
Natural	coded	-1	0	+1	interval
Water expenditure, kg/m³	x_1	155	165	175	10
Cement expenditure, kg/m³	x_2	270	340	410	70
Sand portion in the aggregates' mix (r)					
Cement strength, Mpa	x_3	0.35	0.40	0.45	0.05
	x_4	37.0	45.0	53.0	8.0

After carrying out the experiments and data processing using statistical analysis, mathematical models of fresh concrete mix workability by Vebe ($\hat{y}_1$), sec and hardened concrete strength ($\hat{y}_2$) with adequate confidence probability of 95% are obtained:

$$\hat{y}_1 = 13.4 - 9.97\,x_1 + 3.9\,x_2 + 4.7\,x_3 - 3.1\,x_1\,x_3 + 2.9\,x_2\,x_3 + $$
$$+2.8\,x_1^2 + 0.97\,x_2^2 + 5.1\,x_3^2 \qquad (4.1)$$

$$\hat{y}_2 = 30.90 - 1.76\,x_1 + 5.01\,x_2 - 1.44\,x_3 + 2.19\,x_4 + 0.95\,x_1\,x_2 - 0.88\,x_2\,x_3 + $$
$$+0.97\,x_2\,x_4 - 0.92\,x_2^2 - 1.47\,x_3^2 \qquad (4.2)$$

Differentiation of the equation $\hat{y}_1$ by x_3 (optimization factor) yields:

$$x_3 = \frac{3.1x_1 - 2.9x_2 - 4.7}{10.2} \qquad (4.3)$$

By simultaneous solution of Eqs. (4.1...4.3), compositions with minimum water and cement expenditures for optimal aggregates' ratio providing the required workability of the mix and hardened concrete strength are found.

Based on the models' solution nomograms, allowing selection of optimal concrete compositions, corresponding to the given conditions, were obtained. For example, if it is required to obtain a composition, providing $R_{cmp} = 30$ MPa, workability by Vebe Vb=20 sec and R_{cem}=40 MPa, from Figure 4.1 follows that the contents of cement and water should be 328 kg/m³ and 152 kg/m³, respectively, and r=0.36 (Figure 4.2).

Using the absolute volumes method, the contents of sand and crushed stone are found.

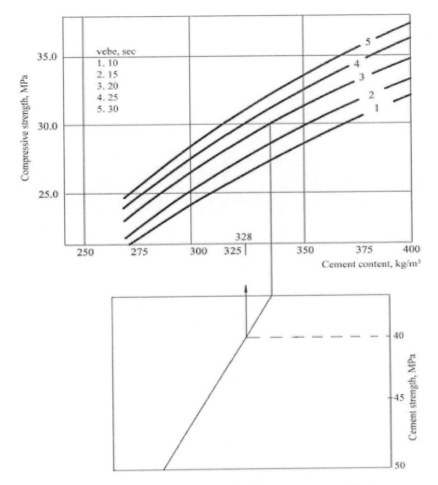

Figure 4.1. Nomogram for determining cement content vs. concrete ultimate compressive strength R$_{cmp}$ and cement strength R$_{cem}$.

Example 4.2. Design optimum concrete mix compositions at normal hardening and steaming for cements with different ultimate strength and aggregates with various water consumption. Workability of concrete mix and concrete strength are given.

Creating an adequate model of concrete mix workability is available in a relatively narrow range of Vebe time or slump. Therefore, to optimize a wide range of concrete compositions, it is more suitable to create a model of concrete mix water consumption at optimum sand portion in a mixture of aggregates (*r*) and planned workability.

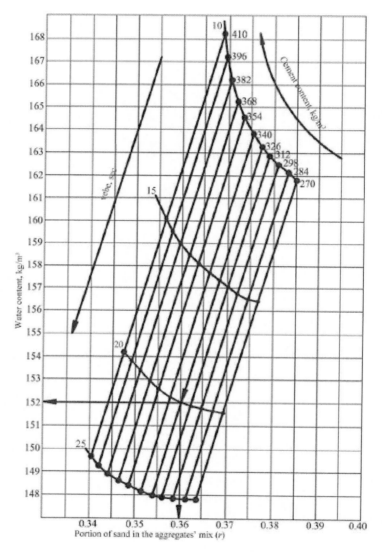

Figure 4.2. Nomogram for determining water content and portion of sand in the aggregates' mix (*r*).

To solve concrete compositions design problems for concrete of normal and rapid hardening experiments were carried out according to second-order Ha_5 and B_4 plans (Table 8, 10 Appendices), which require relatively small number of experiments.

The purpose of choosing the variation intervals (Table 4.2) was the properties description in a rather broad region of concrete mix compositions, including high-slump, low-slump and no-slump mixtures. For this reason, the following workability scale was used:

Conditional score	0		0.6	1	1.4	1.8	2
Workability	10 sec		2 cm	5 cm	8 cm	11 cm	13 cm
	Vebe time		Cone slump				

Table 4.2. Conditions of experiments' planning

Factors		Variation levels			Variation interval
Natural form	Coded form	-1	0	1	
Water content of the concrete mix, kg/m³	x_1	150	180	210	30
Cement-water ratio	x_2	1.3	2.1	2.9	0.8
Water consumption of crushed stone, %	x_3	1.0	4.0	7.0	3.0
Water consumption of sand, %	x_4	4.0	9.0	14.0	5.0
Cement paste normal consistency, %	x_5	24.6	27.2	29.8	
Cement strength, MPa	x_6	34.5	43.2	51.9	8.7
Duration of heat treatment, hours	x_7	10.0	14.0	18.0	4.0
Conditional workability	x_8	2.0	1.0	0.0	1.0
Temperature of isothermal heating, °C	x_9	65.0	80.0	95.0	15.0

Varied according to Table 4.2, water consumptions of sand and crushed stone are the integral quantitative indexes of their influence on concrete mix and hardened concrete properties. They are determined by the comparative tests of cement paste, mortar and concrete mixes. For determining the water consumption of sand $S_{w.c.}$ the water-cement ratio of the cement paste $(W/C)_p$ is set to show 170 mm on the flow table, which approximately corresponds to normal consistency. Then the water-cement ratio of cement-sand mortar

$(W/C)_m$ is determined for cement : sand = 1:2 for the investigated sand, at which it has a same flow. Water consumption of sand (%) can be calculated as follows:

$$S_{w.c} = \frac{(W/C)_m - (W/C)_p}{2} 100.$$ (4.4)

For determining the water consumption of crushed stone $((Cr.S_{w.c})$, water-cement ratio of concrete mixture $(W/C)_c$ for cement : sand : crushed stone = 1:2:3.5 yielding the same slump as the cement-sand mortar with $(W/C)_m$, is obtained.

The water consumption of crushed stone can be calculated as

$$Cr.S_{w.c} = \frac{(W/C)_c - (W/C)_m}{2} 100.$$ (4.5)

Quantitative dependences in the form of adequate mathematical models of concrete and concrete mixes' properties are presented in Table 4.3.

Table 4.3. Mathematical models of concrete and concrete mixes' properties

Properties	Equation type	
Optimal portion of sand in the aggregates' mix	$\hat{y}_1 = 0.305 + 0.012x_1 - 0.044x_2 + 0.009x_3 - 0.039x_4 + 0.003x_1^2 + 0.017x_2^2 + 0.010x_3^2 + 0.005x_4^2 - 0.004x_5^2 + 0.007x_2x_4 - 0.008x_2x_5$	(4.6)
Water consumption of the concrete mix, kg/m³	$\hat{y}_2 = 86.0 + 28.9x_8 + 10.3x_2 + 21.5x_3 + 14.1x_4 + 9.1x_5 - 2.7x_8^2 + 6.8x_2^2 + 11.3x_3^2 + 7.8x_4^2 + 5.3x_5^2 + 1.6x_8x_4 + 2.1x_8x_5 + 2.1x_3x_4 - 2.4x_3x_5$	(4.7)
Compressive strength, four hours after heat treatment, Mpa	$\hat{y}_3 = 24.73 - 1.58x_8 + 12.0x_2 - 0.62x_5 + 3.66x_6 + 3.2x_7 + 2.06x_9 - 0.4x_8^2 - 0.6x_2^2 - 0.4x_5^2 + 0.15x_6^2 - 1.15x_7^2 - 0.6x_9^2 - 1.2x_8x_2 - 0.65x_8x_5 + 0.67x_8x_7 + 2.79x_2x_6 + 1.15x_2x_7$	(4.8)
Compressive strength of steamed concrete at 28 days, Mpa	$\hat{y}_4 = 31.96 - 1.63x_8 + 12.21x_2 - 0.69x_5 + 4.0x_6 + 2.13x_7 - 0.74x_9 - 0.3x_8^2 - 1.25x_2^2 - 0.4x_5^2 + 0.05x_6^2 - 0.15x_7^2 - 1.45x_9^2 - 0.98x_8x_6 - 1.67x_8x_6 + 1.01x_2x_7 + 0.99x_2x_9 + 2.64x_2x_6$	(4.9)
Compressive strength of concrete after normal hardening at 28 days, MPa	$\hat{y}_5 = 40.08 - 0.85x_8 + 13.96x_2 - 0.6x_5 + 4.7x_6 - 0.43x_8^2 - 1.73x_2^2 - 0.35x_5^2 - 0.03x_6^2 - 1.59x_8x_2 - 1.3x_8x_6 + 2.59x_2x_6$	(4.10)

Design of the concrete mixture composition can be performed by joint solution of the obtained mathematical models. The required C/W ratio (x_2) is determined from the strength model ($_5$). For steamed concrete, the higher of two obtained C/W values for models ($_4$) and ($_3$) strengths is selected. Then, the concrete mix water consumption W ($_2$) is calculated. In the case if plasticizers are added, ($_2$) should be adjusted taking into account the coefficients from Table 4.4.

Cement content can be calculated by the formula:

$$C = W \cdot C / W. \qquad (4.11)$$

The sand (S) and crushed stone (Cr.S) contents are determined using the absolute volumes method after calculation of the optimal portion of sand in a mixture of aggregates (r) from model $_1$:

$$S = (1000 - C/\rho_c - W/\rho_w) \cdot r \, \rho_s; \qquad (4.12)$$

$$Cr.S = (1000 - C/\rho_c - W/\rho_w - S/\rho_s) \cdot \rho_{cr.s} \qquad (4.13)$$

where ρ_w, ρ_c, ρ_s, $\rho_{cr.s}$ are the densities of water, cement, sand and crushed stone, kg/l.

Concrete mixture composition design can be also performed using the nomograms (Figures 4.3...4.6). Figures 4.3 and 4.4 can be used for determining the required C/W for concrete with normal and accelerated hardening, respectively. According to the nomogram in Figures 4.5 and 4.6, the required water content and the optimal portion of sand in the aggregates mix are obtained. Then, using the method of absolute volumes, the sand and crushed stone contents are calculated.

The following two examples demonstrate solution of such problem using nomograms.

Example 4.2-a. Design a concrete mix composition with slump of 5...9 cm for concrete with ultimate compressive strength $R_{cmp} = 20$ MPa. For concrete production are used: Portland cement (cement strength equals 50 MPa, paste normal consistency NC = 27%; $\rho_c = 3{,}1$ kg/l), quartz sand (water consumption $S_{w.c} = 9\%$, $\rho_s = 2{,}6$ kg/l), crushed stone (water consumption $Cr.S_{w.c} = 4\%$, $\rho_{cr.s} = 2{,}65$ kg/l), quantity of naphtalene-formaldehyde superplasticizer is 0,7 % of the cement weight.

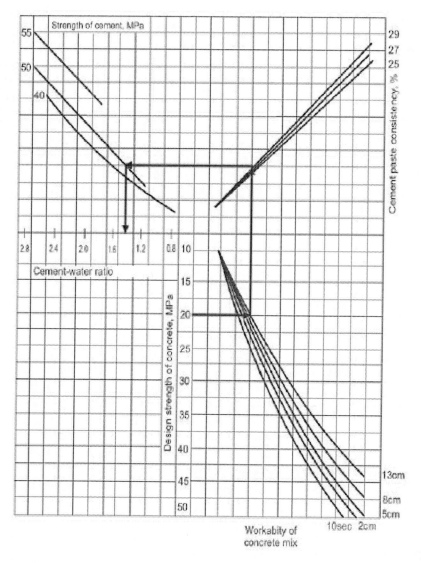

Figure 4.3. Nomogram for determining the cement-water ratio in normal hardened concrete.

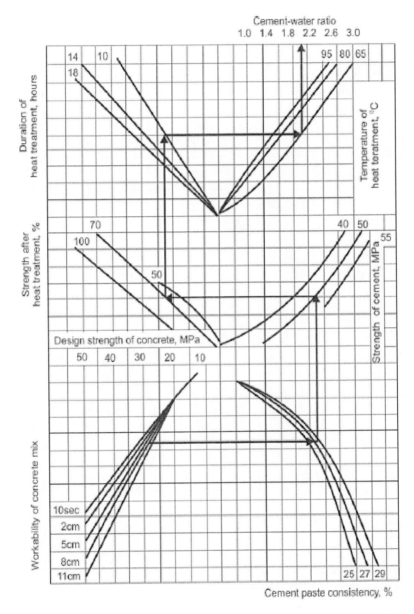

Figure 4.4. Nomogram for determining the cement-water ratio of concrete subjected to heat treatment.

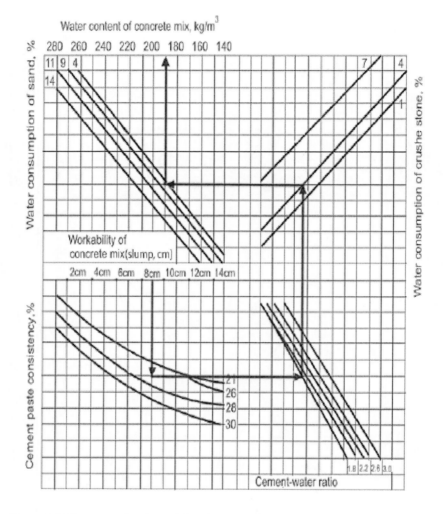

Figure 4.5. Nomogram for determining the concrete mix water consumption.

Following the nomogram given in Figure 4.3, the required C/W = 1.4. The water expenditure (Figure 4.5) is 190 l/m^3, and taking into account the correction coefficient (see Table 4.4), W = 190 · 0.82 = 156 kg/m^3.

The cement expenditure is: C = 156·1.4 = 219 kg/m^3.

The optimal portion of sand in the aggregates' mix is obtained according Figure 4.6, $r = 0.38$.

The sand and crushed stone expenditures are calculated as follows:

$$S = (1000 - \frac{2,19}{3.1} - \frac{156}{1}) \cdot 0.38 \cdot 2.6 = 764 \ \text{kg/m}^3$$

$$Cr.S = (1000 - \frac{219}{3.1} - \frac{156}{1} - \frac{764}{2.6}) \cdot 2.65 = 1271 \ \text{kg/m}^3$$

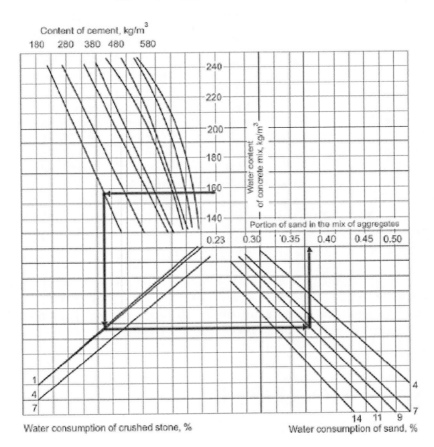

Figure 4.6. Nomogram for determining the optimal portion of sand in the aggregates' mix.

Table 4.4. Water content correction coefficients for concrete mixes with plasticizers

Mix workability		Cement–water ratio				
Slump, cm	Workability (Vebe time); sec	1.40	1.80	2.20	2.60	3.0
-	30...50	0.96	0.95	0.94	0.93	0.92
		0.88	0.85	0.83	0.81	0.80
1...4	-	0.93	0.92	0.92	0.92	0.91
		0.86	0.84	0.82	0.80	0.79
5...9	-	0.91	0.91	0.90	0.90	0.89
		0.82	0.80	0.79	0.78	0.77
10...15	-	0.90	0.89	0.88	0.87	0.87
		0.80	0.78	0.77	0.76	0.75

Note. Numerator denotes values, calculated using the technical lignosulphonates admixture (0.25% of cement weight), denominator denotes values, calculated using the naphtalene-formaldehyde superplasticizer (0.7% of cement weight).

Example 4.2.-b. Design a composition of steamed concrete, providing after heat treatment 70% of ultimate compressive strength R_{cmp}=30 MPa (duration of steaming τ=10 hours, temperature of steaming T = 65°C).

For production of concrete are used the same initial materials as in example 4.2.-a. The concrete mix slump should be 5...9 cm. Plasticizer is not added. Portland cement with strength 50 MPa (ρ_c= 3.1 kg/l, paste normal consistency NC = 27%), quartz sand (water consumption $S_{w.c}$ = 11%, ρ_s = 2.6 kg/l), crushed stone (water consumption $Cr.S_{w.c}$ = 1%; $\rho_{cr.s}$ = 2.65 kg/l).

Following the nomogram given in Figure 4.4, the required C/W=2.1. Water content W (Figure 4.5) is 190 kg/m^3 and content of cement

$$C = 190 \cdot 2.1 = 399 \text{ kg/m}^3.$$

An optimal portion of sand in the aggregates' mix is found using Figure 4.6: $r = 0.34$.

Sand and crushed granite expenditures are:

$$S = (1000 - \frac{399}{3.1} - \frac{190}{1}) \cdot 0.34 \cdot 2.6 = 602 \ \text{kg/m}^3;$$

$$Cr.S = (1000 - \frac{399}{3.1} - \frac{190}{1} - \frac{602}{2.6}) \cdot 2.65 = 1192 \ \text{kg/m}^3$$

Example 4.3. Design compositions of slag-containing self-compacting concrete with ultimate compressive strength $R_{cmp}=15...35$ MPa, providing after heat treatment maximum cement efficiency coefficient (R_{cmp}/C), where C – cement content, kg/m^3.

For solving this problem, a complex of mathematical models for properties of slag-containing self-compacting concrete and nomograms was obtained (Tables 4.5 and 4.6, Figure. 4.7 and 4.8). In design of concrete compositions, first the cement-water ratio is calculated from the conditions of providing the concrete strength at 28 days after heat treatment ($\hat{y}_3$) and concrete strength at four hours after heat treatment ($\hat{y}_2$) (Figure 4.7).

Table 4.5. Conditions of experiment planning

Factors		Variation levels			Variation interval
Natural	Coded	-1	0	+1	
Portion of crushed stone in the aggregates' mix $r_{cr.s}$	x_1	0	0.33	0.66	0.33
Portion of slag in the fine aggregates r'_{sl}	x_2	0	0.5	1.0	0.5
Water consumption of crushed stone, %	x_3	1.5	2.5	3.5	1.0
Water consumption of slag, %	x_4	7.0	9.0	11.0	2.0
Water consumption of sand, %	x_5	5.0	10.0	15.0	5.0
Cement-water ratio	x_6	1.3	1.9	2.5	0.6

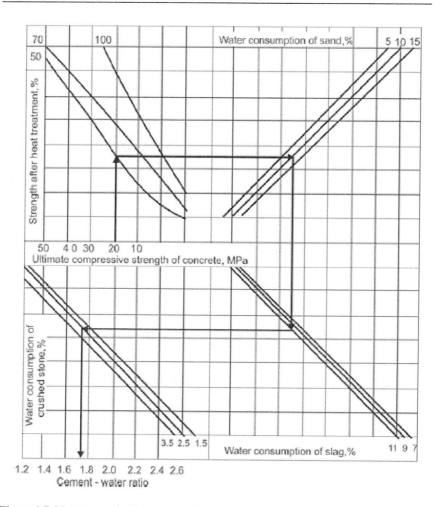

Figure 4.7. Nomogram for determining the cement-water ratio.

The crushed stone and slag contents are calculated using formulas obtained by simultaneous solution of models $\hat{y}_4$, $\hat{y}_5$ under a condition of providing a maximum cement efficiency coefficient depending on the concrete strength at four hours after heat treatment $\partial \hat{y}_4 / \partial x_1 = 0$ and $\partial \hat{y}_4 / \partial x_2 = 0$.

for 70% strength, four hours after heat treatment:

$$x_1 = 0.456 - 0.036x_3 + 0.027x_4 - 0.082x_5 + 0.05x_6$$

$$x_2 = 0.006 + 0.028x_3 + 0.024x_4 + 0.048x_5 + 0.027x_6 \qquad (4.14)$$

for 50% strength, four hours after heat treatment:

$$x_1 = 0.470 - 0.081x_3 - 0.020x_4 - 0.105x_5 + 0.154x_6$$
$$x_2 = 0.088 - 0.015x_3 - 0.035x_4 - 0.011x_5 + 0.144x_6 \qquad (4.15)$$

The required water content for achieving a self-compacting mix is obtained using the $\hat{y}_1$ model or from the nomogram given in Figure 4.8 that was received by processing the calculated results according to this model.

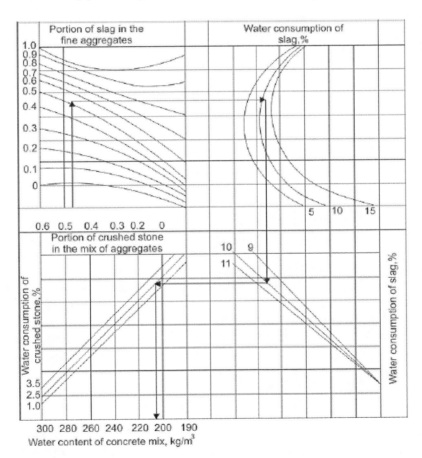

Figure 4.8. Nomogram for determining the concrete mix water consumption.

Contents of sand (S), crushed stone (Cr.S) and slag (Sl) are obtained as follows:

$$r = 1 - r_{cr.s} \tag{4.16}$$

where r and $r_{cr.s}$ are portions of fine and coarse aggregates in the aggregates' mix.

$$r_s = r - r_{sl} \tag{4.17}$$

where r_s and r_{sl} are portions of sand and slag in the aggregates' mix.

$$r_{sl} = r'_{sl} r \tag{4.18}$$

where r'_{sl} is portion of slag in the fine aggregate.

$$Cr.S = (r_{cr.s} \, V_{aggr}) \rho_{cr.s} \tag{4.19}$$

$$Sl = (r_{sl} \, V_{aggr}) \rho_{sl} \tag{4.20}$$

$$S = (r_s \, V_{aggr}) \rho_s \tag{4.21}$$

where V_{aggr} are aggregates' volume; ρ_w, ρ_c, ρ_s, ρ_{sl}, $\rho_{cr.s}$ are the densities of water, cement, sand, slag and crushed stone, kg/l.

For example, determine a slag-containing self-compacting concrete composition with ultimate concrete compressive strength $R_{cmp} = 20$ MPa and 50 % strength at four hours after heat treatment. Initial materials: Portland cement with strength 40 MPa ($\rho_c = 3.1$ kg/l, paste normal consistency NC = 27%), quartz sand (water consumption $S_{w.c} = 10$ %, $\rho_s = 2.69$ kg/l), crushed stone (water consumption $Cr.S_{w.c} = 2.5$ %, $\rho_{cr.s} = 2.61$ kg/l), fuel slag (water consumption $Sl_{w.c} = 9$%, $\rho_{sl} = 2.45$ kg/l), superplasticizer (Sp) content equal to 0.7 % of the cement weight.

Following Figure 4.7, the required C/W = 1.72. According to Eq.(4.15), the optimal portion of crushed stone in the aggregates' mix and the portion of slag in the fine aggregate are:

$x_1 = 0.470 - 0.081 \cdot 0 - 0.020 \cdot 0 - 0.015 \cdot 0 + 0.154 \cdot (-0.33) = 0.419$
$x_2 = 0.088 - 0.015 \cdot 0 - 0.035 \cdot 0 - 0.011 \cdot 0 + 0144 \cdot (-0.33) = 0.040$

Table 4.6. Mathematical models of slag-containing self-compacting concrete properties

Properties	Equation type	
Concrete mix water consumption, kg/m^3	$\hat{y}_1 = 208.6 - 7.7x_1 - 3.4x_2 - 5.5x_3 + 8.4x_4 + 2.5x_5 +$ $10x_6 + 17x^2_1 + 26.5x^2_2 + 1.5x^2_3 - 1.0x^2_4 +$ $12.1x_1x_2 + 5.6x_1x_3 - 5.1x_1x_5 + 8.5x_2x_4 - 10x_2x_5$	(4.22)
Compressive strength, four hours after heat treatment, MPa	$\hat{y}_2 = 18.9 + 2.1x_1 + x_2 + 0.4x_3 + 0.5x_4 + +0.5x_5 +$ $8.9x_6 - 0.8x^2_1 - 2x^2_2 + 0.3x^2_3 -$ $0.7x^2_4 + 1.1x^2_5 + 1.5x^2_6 - 1.3x_1x_3 -$ $0.3x_1x_5 + 0.7x_1x_6 - 0.3x_2x_3 + 0.3x_2x_4 -$ $0.2x_2x_5 + 0.7x_2x_6 - 0.9x_3x_4 - 0.3x_3x_5 - 0.8x_4x_5$	(4.23)
Concrete compressive strength, 28 days after heat treatment, MPa	$\hat{y}_3 = 30.9 + 2.6x_1 + 2.5x_2 + 1.3x_3 + 1.8x_4 + 1.8x_5 +$ $13x_6 + 0.4x^2_1 - 1.5x^2_2 + 1.3x^2_3 -$ $1.0x^2_4 + 0.9x^2_5 - 0.8x^2_6 - 1.4x_1x_2 - 0.6x_1x_3$ $0.8x_1x_4 - 0.8x_1x_5 + 2x_1x_6 + 1.1x_2x_3 -$ $1.3x_2x_5 + 2.4x_2x_6 - 0.3x_3x_4 - 0.4x_3x_5 - 0.3x_4x_5$	(4.24)
Cement efficiency coefficient for concrete, four hours after heat treatment	$\hat{y}_4 = 0.415 + 0.065x_1 + 0.016x_2 + 0.005x_3 + 0.069x_4 -$ $0.071x^2_1 - 0.080x^2_2 + 0.009x^2_3 -$ $0.010x^2_4 + 0.02x^2_5 - 0.009x^2_6 - 0.033x_1x_2 - 0.02x_1x_3 -$ $0.010x_1x_5 + 0.008x_1x_6 + +0.009x_2x_3 + 0.005x_2x_5 +$ $0.006x_2x_6 - 0.010x_3x_4 - 0.015x_3x_5 - 0.007x_3x_6 -$ $0.010x_4x_5 - 0.008x_4x_6 - 0.005x_5x_6$	(4.25)
Cement efficiency coefficient for concrete, 28 days after heat treatment	$\hat{y}_5 = 0.772 + 0.082x_1 - 0.015x_2 + 0.008x_3 + 0.006x_5 +$ $0.095x_6 - 0.028x^2_1 - 0.118x^2_2 -$ $0.021x^2_3 + 0.026x^2_4 - 0.043x^2_5 - 0.003x^2_6 -$ $0.050x_1x_2 + 0.013x_1x_4 - 0.021x_1x_5 - 0.005x_2x_5$ $+0.009x_2x_6 + 0.010x_3x_4 - 0.015x_3x_5 - 0.021x_3x_6 +$ $0.008x_4x_5 - 0.009x_4x_6 - 0.029x_5x_6$	(4.26)

In natural units:

$r_{cr.s} = 0.33 \cdot 0.419 + 0.33 = 0.47$

$r'_{sl} = 0.5 \cdot 0.040 + 0.5 = 0.52$

The water content is obtained according to Figure 4.8:

W = 208 kg/m^3

The cement content:

$C = 208 \cdot 1.72 = 358 \text{ kg/m}^3$

Superplasticizer content:

$Sp = 358 \cdot 0.007 = 2.51 \text{ kg/m}^3$

The optimal portions of fine aggregate (r), slag r_{sl} and sand r_s in the aggregates' mix are obtained using Eqs. (4.14...4.16):

$r = 1\text{-}0.47 = 0.53;\ r_{sl} = 0.53 \cdot 0.52 = 0.28;\ r_s = 0.53 - 0.28 = 0.25$

Contents of crushed stone (Cr.S), slag (Sl) and sand (S) are obtained using Eqs. (4.19...4.21):

$$Cr.S = (1 - 0.53)(1000 - \frac{358}{3.1} - \frac{208}{1})2.61 = 830 \text{ kg} / m^3,$$

$$Sl = 0.28(1000 - \frac{358}{3.1} - \frac{208}{1})2.45 = 464 \text{ kg} / m^3,$$

$$S = 0.25(1000 - \frac{358}{3.1} - \frac{208}{1})2.69 = 455 \text{ kg} / m^3.$$

4.2. EXAMPLES OF MULTI-PARAMETRIC DESIGN OF CONCRETE COMPOSITIONS

Example 4.4. Design optimum compositions of hydraulic concrete with specified values of strength, frost resistance and water impermeability at normal hardening and heat treatment.

The initial materials are: Portland cement; crushed granite; quartz sand with fineness modulus of 2.1. An air-entraining admixture is used.

When steaming samples, isothermal curing temperature is 80°C. Within the overall heat-humidity treatment durations of 14...18 and 10 hours, the preliminary curing are five and three hours, respectively. The temperature rising speed in the chamber is 15°C per hour. Conditions of planning experiments are presented in Table 4.7.

Minimization of cement content for the designed concrete compositions is achieved at optimum portion of sand in the aggregates mix (r_{opt}), ensuring the minimum water consumption of the concrete mixes. To find r_{opt} by processing the results of experiments, performed according to the Ha_5 plan (Table 10, Appendices), special quadratic model is created (Table 4.8).

Table 4.7. Conditions of experiments planning

Factors		Variation levels			Variation intervals
Natural	Coded	-1	0	+1	
Initial water content, kg/m^3	x_1	150	180	210	30
Cement-water ratio	x_2	1.3	2.1	2.9	0.8
Maximum crushed stone coarseness, mm	x_3	10	40	70	30
Content of air-entraining admixture, kg/m^3	x_4	0	0.06	0.12	0.06
Cement paste normal consistency, %	x_5	24.6	27.2	29.8	2.6
Cement strength, MPa	x_6	34.5	41.2	47.9	6.7
Heat-humidity treatment duration, hours	x_7	10	14	18	4
Conditional workability	x_8	-1	0	+1	1
Normal hardening duration, days*	x_9	lg 28	lg 71	lg 180	2
Cement content, kg/m^3	x_{10}	234	378	522	144

Note: * For simplification of the proper models, lg τ was used; τ is duration of hardening, days.

Table 4.8. Mathematical models of concrete mixes' properties

Properties	Equation type	
Entrained air volume, %	$\hat{y}_1 = 2.27 + 0.72x_1 - 0.63x_{10} - 0.47x_3 + 2.14x_4 -$ $0.18x_5 - 0.20x^2{}_1 + 0.24x^2{}_{10} + 0.17x^2{}_3 - 0.22x^2{}_4 -$ $0.09x^2{}_5 - 0.13x_1x_2 + 0.71x_1x_4 - 0.61x_{10}x_4 -$ $- 0.46x_3x_4 - 0.13x_3x_5 - 0.19x_4x_5$	(4.27)
Concrete mix water consumption, kg/m^3	$\hat{y}_2 = 169.2 + 26.4x_8 + 13.4x_2 - 20x_3 - 8.3x_4 +$ $9.3x_5 - 5.2x^2{}_8 + 5.8x^2{}_2 + 8.8x^2{}_3 + 2.8x^2{}_4 +$ $3.8x^2{}_5 + x_8x_3 + 2.6x_8x_5 - x_2x_3 + 3.1x_2x_4 + 2.25x_2x_5 -$ $1.1x_3x_5 + x_4x_5$	(4.28)
Optimal portion of sand in aggregates' mix	$\hat{y}_3 = 0.284 + 0.03x_1 - 0.039x_2 - 0.02x_3 + 0.009x_4$ $+0.007x^2{}_1 + 0.016x^2{}_2 + 0.008x^2{}_3 + 0.006x^2{}_4 -$ $0.005x_1x_2 + 0.01x_1x_3 + 0.009x_2x_4 - 0.004x_3x_4$	(4.29)

Additionally, quadratic models for concrete mixes' water consumption and entrained air volume were obtained (Table 4.8). In the water consumption model (Table 4.9), the conditional workability values (x_8) were planned:

Table 4.9. Planning of conditional workability values

Variation levels	-1	-0,4	0	+0,4	+1
Workability score	Vebe time, sec		Slump, cm		
	20	8	2	5	13

In the model (4.27) of entrained air volume, instead of C/W (x_2), the cement content C (x_{10}) was varied (Table 4.7).

Six-factorial models of compressive strength, frost resistances and water impermeability, considering concrete mix workability (x_8), C/W (x_2), content of air-entraining admixture (x_4), as well as duration of normal (x_9) and accelerated hardening (x_7), were obtained for normal hardened and steamed concretes.

Table 4.10. Mathematical models of normal hardened concrete properties

Properties	Equation type	
Compressive strength, MPa	$\hat{y}_4= 36.93 - 1.88x_8 + 14.73x_2 - 3.62x_4 - 0.86x_5$ $+ +4.97x_6+ 6.08x_9 - 0.05x^2_8 - 1.85x^2_2 - 0.2x^2_4$ $- 0.3x^2_5 + +0.05x^2_6 - 0.8x^2_9 - 0.61x_8x_4 -$ $0.45x_8x_5 + 1.23x_8x_6 + +0.97x_2x_4 - 0.63x_2x_5 +$ $2.12x_2x_6 + 2.14x_2x_9 + 0.99x_4x_6 - -0.46x_5x_6 +$ $0.88x_6x_9$	(4.30)
Frost resistance, cycles	$\hat{y}_5 = 378.9 - 67.8x_8 +162.3x_2 + 147.7x_4 -$ $27.4x_5 + +21.8x_6 + 63.2x_9 + 9.7x^2_8 - 38.8x^2_2 +$ $6.7x^2_4 - 9.8x^2_5 + +11.7x^2_6 + 2.2x^2_9 + 29.4x_8x_2$ $- 8.7x_8x_5 - 16.6x_8x_9 + +26.6x_2x_4 - 15.8x_2x_5 +$ $18.7x_2x_9 + 7.1x_4x_6 + 23.7x_4x_9 + +13.8x_6x_9$	(4.31)
Water impermeability, MPa	$\hat{y}_6= 0.92 + 0.04x_8 + 0.56x_2 + 0.02x_4 + 0.01x_5$ $+0.06x_6 + 0.25x_9 - 0.05x^2_8 + 0.08x^2_2 - 0.01x^2_4$ $+0.004x^2_5 + 0.03x^2_6 - 0.02x_8x_2 + 0.01x_8x_4 -$ $0.02x_8x_5 + +0.04x_2x_6 + 0.14x_2x_9$	(4.32)

Using a complex of polynomial models allows a relatively easy solution of the concrete composition optimization problem in a wide range of given parameters of properties. The essence of the method is that models $\hat{y}_4$, $\hat{y}_5$, $\hat{y}_6$, $\hat{y}_7$, $\hat{y}_8$, $\hat{y}_9$, $\hat{y}_{10}$ are solved regarding C/W, whereas other factors are fixed at required levels and the values of necessary strength, frost resistances and water impermeability are given. C/W, providing all the required properties, is found. Then, the water consumption and the optimal portion of sand in the mixture of aggregates are obtained using $\hat{y}_2$ and $\hat{y}_3$ models. After that, cement, sand and crushed stone contents per 1 m^3 of concrete mixture are calculated using the absolute volumes method.

Table 4.11. Mathematical models of concrete properties after heat treatment

Properties	Equation type	
Compressive strength at four hours after heat treatment, MPa	$\hat{y}_7 = 21.98 - 0.93x_8 + 10.5x_2 - 1.03x_4 - 1.61x_5 + 2.32x_6 + 2.65x_7 - 0.49x^2_8 - 0.81x^2_2 - 0.09x^2_5 - 0.06x^2_6 - 0.96x^2_7 - 2.00x_8x_2 - 0.88x_8x_4 - 1.36x_8x_5 - 1.43x_8x_6 + 2.68x_2x_6 + 2.60x_2x_7 - 0.91x_4x_5 - 0.82x_4x_6 - 1.01x_4x_7 + 1.18x_5x_7 + 1.22x_6x_7$	(4.33)
Compressive strength at 28 days after heat treatment, MPa	$\hat{y}_8 = 30.6 - 2.24x_8 + 13.03x_2 - 2.86x_4 - 0.99x_5 + 3.97x_6 + 1.94x_7 - 0.05x^2_8 - 1.75x^2_2 - 0.5x^2_4 - 0.35x^2_5 + 0.1x^2_6 - 0.2x^2_7 - 1.29x_8x_2 + 1.18x_2x_4 - 0.63x_2x_5 + 2.71x_2x_6 + 0.97x_2x_7$	(4.34)
Frost resistance, cycles	$\hat{y}_9 = 281.9 - 38.3x_8 + 145.4x_2 + 89.2x_4 - 16x_5 + 17.7x_7 + 8.3x^2_8 - 15.7x^2_2 - 12.2x^2_4 - 5.2x^2_5 + 9.3x^2_6 - 2.2x^2_7 - 13.3x_8x_2 + 14.8x_8x_4 + 7.3x_2x_4 + 21.2x_6x_7$	(4.35)
Water impermeability, Mpa	$\hat{y}_{10} = 0.57 + 0.07x_8 + 0.43x_2 + 0.03x_5 + 0.06x_6 + 0.05x_7 - 0.02x^2_8 + 0.08x^2_2 + 0.02x^2_4 - 0.06x^2_7 + 0.07x_8x_2 + 0.03x_8x_2 - 0.04x_2x_4 + 0.03x_2x_5 + 0.06x_2x_6 - 0.02x_4x_6 - 0.02x_4x_7 + 0.01x_5x_6 + 0.02x_6x_7$	(4.36)

Consider specific examples for optimum concrete compositions design using mathematic models, given in Tables 4.8...4.10.

Example 4.4-a. Design the hydraulic concrete compositions used in structures at 28 and 180 days of normal hardening.

Nomograms shown in Figures 4.9, 4.10 and 4.11 were created according to calculations, performed using the mathematical models (Tables 4.7, 4.9, 4.10). These nomograms can be used to determine the water content, C/W and *r* for given conditions. The established approximate relations of normal hardening concrete properties (Table 4.10) and coefficients for correction of C/W at 180 days (Table 4.12) are used also.

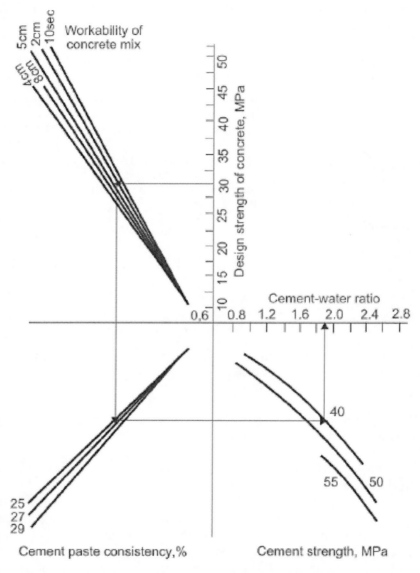

Figure4.9. Nomogram for determining the cement-water ratio for concrete at 28 days (without air-entraining admixture).

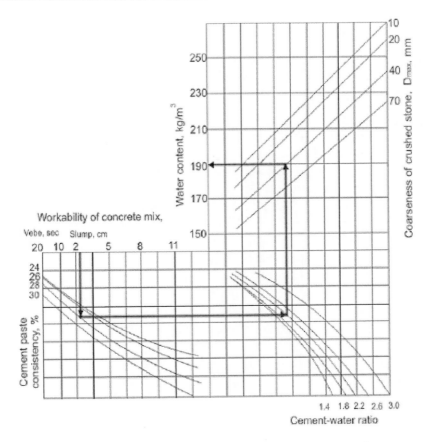

Figure 4.10. Nomogram for determining water consumption of concrete mixtures

Additionally, a nomogram for determining the portion of sand in the aggregates' mix (Figure 4.11) is corrected, taking into account experimental results, characterizing the influence of sand fineness modulus.

For example, Portland cement with strength of 40 MPa (ρ_c = 3,1 kg/l, paste normal consistency NC = 28 %), quartz sand (fineness modulus M_f=2.2, ρ_s = 2,6 kg/l), crushed granite of fraction 5...40 mm ($\rho_{cr.s}$ = 2,65 kg/l) and admixture of technical lignosulphonates 0.25 % by cement weight are used for production of concrete with minimum ultimate strength of 20 MPa, frost resistance of 150 freezing and thawing cycles and water impermeability of 0.2 MPa in an age of 28 days, the concrete mixture's slump should be 1...2 cm.

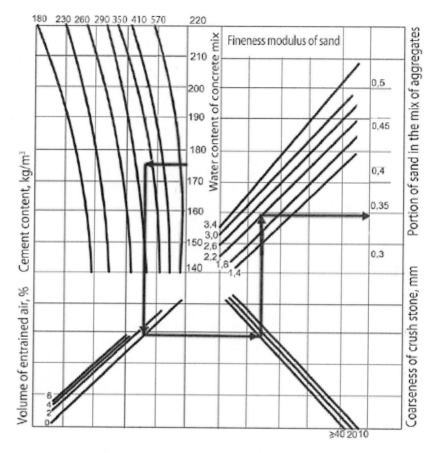

Figure 4.11. Nomogram for determining the portion of sand in aggregates' mix.

According to Table 4.12, the ultimate concrete strength, providing the required frost resistances and water impermeability, is $R_{cmp} = 30$ MPa.

Following Figure 4.9, the required cement-water ratio: C/W = 1.96.

Water content (Figure 4.10) is 190 kg/m³, and considering admixture of technical lignosulphonates (Table 4.4) W = 190 · 0.92 = 175 kg/m³.

Content of cement: C = 175 · 1.96 = 343 kg/m³.

The optimal portion of sand in the aggregates' mix is obtained using Figure 4.11: r = 0.345.

Contents of sand (S) and crushed stone (Cr.S) are:

$$S = \left[1000 - \left(\frac{343}{3.1} + \frac{175}{1.0}\right)\right] \cdot 0.345 \cdot 2.6 = 641 \ \text{kg/m}^3$$

$$Cr.S = \left[1000 - \left(\frac{343}{3.1} + \frac{175}{1.0} + \frac{641}{2.6}\right)\right] \cdot 2.65 = 1240 \ \text{kg/m}^3$$

Table 4.12. Relations between properties of normal hardened concrete without air entraining admixtures

| Mix slump, cm | Concrete strength at | | | | | |
| | 28 days | | | 180 days | | |
	Strength, MPa	Frost resistance, cycles	Water impermeability, MPa	Strength, MPa	Frost resistance, cycles	Water impermeability, MPa
1...4	20	50...75	0.2	20	50...75	0.2...0.4
5...9	20	50...75	0.2	20	50...75	0.2...0.4
10...15	20	50	0.2	20	50	0.2...0.4
1...4	30	100...150	0.2...0.4	30	150...200	0.4...0.6
5...9	30	100	0.2...0.4	30	100...150	0.4...0.6
10...15	30	75...100	0.2...0.4	30	75...100	0.4...0.6
1...4	40	200...250	0.6...0.8	40	250	0.8...1
5...9	40	200...250	0.6...0.8	40	200...250	0.8...1
10...15	40	100...150	0.6...0.8	40	150...200	0.8...1

If the design requirements to concrete should be provided at its age of 180 days, then following Table 4.12, the ultimate concrete strength should also be 30 MPa. The previously defined value of C/W (Figure 4.9) is corrected taking into account appropriate coefficients from Table 4.13;

C/W = 1.96 · 0.73 = 1.43

The water content is 190 kg/m^3 (Figure 4.10) and considering admixture of technical lignosulphonates (Table 4.4) W = 190 · 0.92 = 175 kg/m^3.

Cement content C = 175 · 1.43 = 250 kg/m^3.

The optimal portion of sand in the aggregates' mix is found from Figure 4.11: $r = 0.38$

Table 4.13. Coefficients for correcting C/W at 180 days

Ultimate concrete strength at 28 days, MPa							
15	20	25	30	35	40	45	50
0.96	0.81	0.76	0.73	0.71	0.70	0.68	0.67

Contents of sand and crushed stone are:

$$S = \left[1000 - \left(\frac{250}{3.1} + \frac{175}{1.0} \right) \right] \cdot 0.38 \cdot 2.6 = 735 \ \text{kg/m}^3$$

$$Cr.S = \left[1000 - \left(\frac{250}{3.1} + \frac{175}{1.0} + \frac{735}{2.6} \right) \right] \cdot 2.65 = 1223 \ \text{kg/m}^3$$

Example 4.4-b. Design a composition of hydraulic concrete with different values of strength after heat treatment.

A complex of mathematical models (Table 4.11) enables finding solutions of such problems for any strength after heat treatment, changing the overall heat process duration, mixes workability and cement paste normal consistency in a wide range.

The algorithm for solving this problem differs from the previous just by the fact that either the model for ultimate strength $\hat{y}_8$ or for the strength after heat treatment $\hat{y}_7$ are solved for finding C/W. To determine the cement content, the higher over the two cement-water ratios are selected.

Figure 4.12 represents a nomogram for finding the C/W ratio, providing the ultimate strength and the required concrete mix workability for a given strength after heat treatment. The approximate concrete properties relations are given in Tables 4.14 and 4.16.

For example, for concrete with required compressive strength of 20 MPa, frost resistance F150 and heat treatment duration of 18 hours, the strength after steaming should be 70% of the 28-day one and the concrete mix slump is 1...4 cm.

Portland cement with strength of 40 MPa (paste normal consistency NC = 28 %, $\rho_c = 3.1$ kg/l), quartz sand with fineness modulus $M_f = 2.2$ ($\rho_s = 2.6$ kg/l), crushed granite stone fraction 5...40 mm ($\rho_{cr.s} = 2.65$ kg/l) are used.

Following Table 4.14, for providing the required frost resistance of 150 *freezing and thawing cycles*, the concrete compressive strength should be 25 MPa.

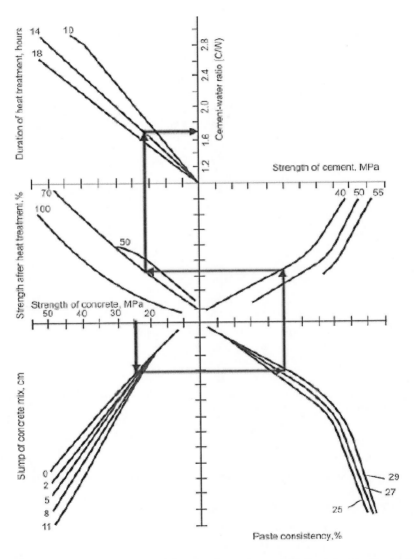

Figure 4.12. Nomogram for determining the cement-water ratio for concrete after heat treatment.

Table 4.14. Relations between properties of concrete without air entraining admixtures, subjected to heat treatment (duration of 14...18 hours)

Concrete compressive strength at 28 days, MPa	Strength after steaming, % of that at 28 days	Frost resistance, cycles	Water impermeability, MPa
15	70	Less than 50	0.2
	100	50...100	0.2
20	50	Less than 50	0.2
	70	50......100	0.2...0.4
	100	100... 150	0.4...0.6
25	50	50... 100	0.2...0.4
	70	100... 150	0.4...0.6
	100	200...250	0.6
30	50	75... 100	0.2...0.4
	70	150... 200	0.4...0.6
	100	200... 250	0.6...0.8
35	50	100... 200 150... 250 200... 300	0.4...0.6
	70		0.6...0.8
	100		0.8...1.0
40	50	150...250	0.6...0.8
	70	200...300	0.8...1.0
	100	300	1.0...1.2

Note. Minimal frost resistance and water impermeability values are given for mixes with slump of 10...15 cm, and maximal values – for mixes with slump of 1...4 cm.

According to Figure 4.12, the required C/W = 1.7. The water content (Figure 4.9) is 190 kg/m^3. The required cement content:

C = 190 · 1.7 = 323 kg/m^3

The optimal sand portion in the aggregates' mix is found using Figure 4.11: $r = 0.38$.

Contents of sand and crushed stone are:

$$S = \left[1000 - \left(\frac{323}{3.1} + \frac{190}{1} \right) \right] \cdot 0.38 \cdot 2.6 = 697 \ \text{kg/m}^3$$

$$Cr.S = \left[1000 - \left(\frac{323}{3.1} + \frac{190}{1} + \frac{697}{2.6}\right)\right] \cdot 2.65 = 1160 \text{ kg/m}^3$$

Example 4.4-c. Design compositions of hydraulic concrete with air-entraining admixture for the conditions described in Example 4.4-a.

Figures 4.13 and 4.14 are given nomograms that can be used for calculating C/W and the air-entraining admixture's content, required for providing the given properties' complex.

Tables 4.15 and 4.16 present the optimal content of the entrained air and coefficients for correction of C/W for concrete with normal curing conditions at 180 days. Water content, obtained using Figure 4.9, is corrected taking into account the entrained air volume.

Table 4.15. Entrained air volume for concrete with different design requirements

Concrete properties			Required volume of entrained air, %
Strength at 28 days, MPa	Frost resistance, cycles	Water impermeability, MPa	
20	100	0.4	1.5...2.0
	150	0.4...0.6	2.5...3.0
	200	0.4...0.6	3.0...3.5
	300	0.4...0.6	3.5...4.0
30	200	0.6	1.5...2.0
	300	0.6...0.8	2.5...3.0
	400	0.6...0.8	3.5...4.0
40	300	0.8...1.0	3.0...3.5
	400	0.8...1.0	3.5...4.0
	500	1.0...1.2	4.5...5.0

Note. Minimal and maximal values of entrained air volume are given for mixes with slump of 1...4 cm and 10...15 cm, respectively.

Following Table 4.15, the entrained air volume for the given concrete design requirements should be 2.5%. The C/W ratio providing the compressive strength of 20 MPa according to Figure 4.9 is 1.5. Following Figure 4.13, the C/W value, corresponding to the optimal air content for the given design properties, is 1.65. For further calculations, the C/W is assumed to be equal to 1.65.

Table 4.16. Correction coefficients for adjusting the cement-water ratio in normal cured concrete with air-entraining admixture at 180 days

Ultimate compressive strength, MPa	Frost resistance, cycles	Correcting coefficient
10	100	0.87
10	200	0.77
15	100	0.80
15	200	0.77
20	100	0.81
20	200... 300	0.77
25	200	0.76
25	300... 400	0.74
30	200	0.76
30	300	0.73
30	400	0.75
35	300... 500	0.72
40	400... 500	0.70
45	500... 600	0.67
50	500... 600	0.67

The water content is obtained according to Figure 4.10 and updated, considering the entrained air volume (water-reducing effect of 1% of entrained air equals approximately 4 liters):

$$W = 190 - (4 \cdot 2.5) = 180 \ l/m^3.$$

The required cement content is:

$$C = 180 \cdot 1.65 = 297 \ kg/m^3.$$

The optimal portion of sand in the aggregates' mix is obtained using Figure 4.11: $r = 0.36$

Sand and crushed stone contents are obtained taking into account the entrained air volume:

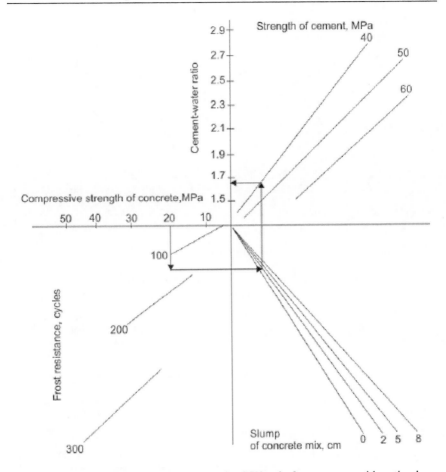

Figure 4.13. A nomogram for determining the C/W ratio for concretes with optimal entrained air content.

$$S = \left[1000 \; - \left(\frac{297}{3.1} + \frac{180}{1} + 25 \right) \right] \cdot 0.36 \cdot 2.6 = 654 \;\; kg \, / \, m^3,$$

$$Cr.S = \left[1000 \; - \left(\frac{297}{3.1} + \frac{180}{1} + 25 + \frac{654}{2.6} \right) \right] \cdot 2.65 = 1186 \;\; kg \, / \, m^3.$$

The content of air entrained admixture equals 0.05 kg/m^3 (Figure 4.14).

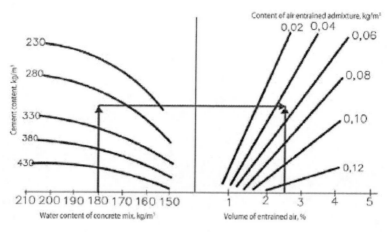

Figure 4.14. A nomogram for defining the air-entraining content.

Example 4.5. Design compositions of normal and accelerated hardened self-compacting ash-containing concrete with given strength, frost resistance and water impermeability.

For solving this problem according to planning conditions (Table 4.17), a complex of mathematical models (Table 4.18) was obtained.

Table 4.17. Conditions of experiments planning

Factors		Variation levels			Variation
Natural	Coded	-1	0	+1	intervals
Specific surface of fly ash, cm²/g	x_1	2900	3900	4900	1000
W/C ratio	x_2	0.5	0.6	0.7	0.1
Water content, kg/m³	x_3	180	190	200	10
Portion of sand in a mix of sand and crushed stone	x_4	0.34	0.41	0.48	0.07
Fly ash content, kg/m³	x_5	50	150	250	100
Portion of crushed stone in a mix of sand, fly ash and crushed stone	x_6	0.45	0.53	0.61	0.08
Portion of fly ash in sand and fly ash volume	x_7	0.1	0.2	0.3	0.1
Fineness modulus of sand	x_8	1.4	2.4	3.4	1.0

Table 4.18. Mathematical models of fly ash containing concrete mix and concrete properties

Properties	Equation type
Superplasticizer's content in concrete mix, kg/m^3	$\hat{y}_1 = 3.28 - 0.07x_1 - 0.94x_2 - 1.06x_3 + 0.37x_4 +$ $+0.7x^2_2 + 0.25x^2_3 + 0.14x^2_4 + 0.23x^2_5 - 0.24x_1x_2 -$ (4.37) $0.25x_1x_4 - 0.32x_1x_5 - 0.17x_3x_5$
Water separation of the concrete mix, g/l	$\hat{y}_2 = 0.37 - 0.35x_1 + 0.51x_2 + 0.75x_3 - 0.56x_4 -$ $0.45x_5 - 0.15x^2_1 + 0.57x^2_3 - 0.15x^2_4 + 0.23x^2_5 -$ $0.09x_1x_2 - 0.09x_1x_3 - 0.22x_1x_5 + 0.41x_2x_3 -$ (4.38) $0.33x_2x_4 - 0.28x_2x_5 - 0.32x_3x_4 - 0.32x_3x_5 + 0.2x_4x_5$
Compressive strength of concrete hardened in normal conditions at 28 days, MPa	$\hat{y}_3 = 28.60 - 5.65x_2 + 2.75x_7 + 2.61x^2_2 - 0.53x^2_3 -$ $2.70x^2_6 - 3.00x^2_7 - 6.50x^2_8 + 1.93x_2x_7 + 0.98x_3x_6$ (4.39)
Concrete compressive strength after heat treatment, MPa	$\hat{y}_4 = 26.4 - 4.65x_2 + 3.6x_7 + 1.6x^2_2 - 0.99x^2_3 -$ $0.19x^2_6 - 1.65x^2_7 - 3.8x^2_8 + 1.35x_2x_7 + 1.06x_3x_6$ (4.40)
Concrete compressive strength 28 days after heat treatment, MPa	$\hat{y}_5 = 29.1 - 7.09x_2 + 3.15x_7 + 3.3x^2_2 - 1.09x^2_3 -$ $0.3x^2_6 - 1.6x^2_7 - 4.5x^2_8 + 1.25x_2x_7 + 0.67x_3x_6$ (4.41)
Frost resistance of concrete, cycles	$\hat{y}_6 = 165 - 57x_2 - 30x_3 + 16x_7 - 6x_8 + 15x^2_2 + 15x^2_3$ $- 11x^2_6 + 10x^2_7 - 18x_2x_6 + 17x_2x_7 +$ (4.42) $+18x_3x_6 + 8x_3x_7 + 11x_3x_8 + 13x_6x_7 + 16x_7x_8$
Water impermeability of concrete, MPa	$\hat{y}_7 = 0.93 - 0.15x_2 + 0.07x_6 + 0.02x^2_2 - 0.04x^2_6 -$ $0.08x^2_7 - 0.03x^2_8 - 0.03x_2x_3 - 0.03x_2x_8 - 0.07x_3x_6 +$ (4.43) $0.03x_3x_7 + 0.03x_6x_7 + 0.05x_7x_8$

The design method for obtaining ash containing concrete compositions is based on a constant ash consumption rule. The optimal ash content for self-compacting concrete is 150...200 kg/m^3. Correction of ash content should take into account the specific conditions of concrete production and use. Simultaneous solution of models for strength $\hat{y}_3$, $\hat{y}_4$, $\hat{y}_5$, frost resistance $\hat{y}_6$ and water impermeability $\hat{y}_7$ allows obtaining the approximate relations of basic concrete design properties at optimal ash content (Table 4.19).

Further solution of the problem reduces obtaining the composition of concrete with required strength, providing the complex of design parameters. With this aim, the required W/C, depending on the required ultimate strength ($\hat{y}_3$) or the strength after heat-humidity treatment ($\hat{y}_5$ or $\hat{y}_4$) are obtained for normal and accelerated hardened concretes, respectively (Figure 4.15).

Table 4.19. Approximate properties relations for self-compacting fly ash containing concrete

Compressive strength, MPa	Frost resistance, cycles	Water impermeability
20	100...150	4...6
25	150...200	6...8
30	200	8...10
35	250	10...12

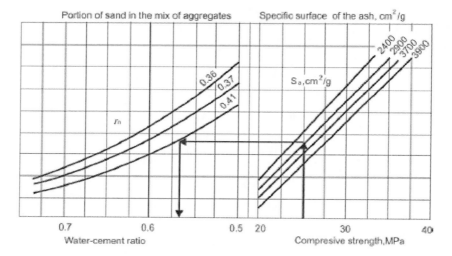

Figure 4.15. Water-cement ratio nomogram.

Minimum water content in concrete mixtures with superplasticizer's addition to achieve a high slump consistency is 180 kg/m^3. Depending on the adopted water content model from $\hat{y}_1$, the required dry superplasticizer content required to ensure the necessary concrete mix consistency is determined (Figure 4.16).

The optimal sand portion value in the sand and crushed stone (r_s) mix is obtained by solving the water separation model y_2 $(\partial \hat{y}_2 / \partial x_4 = 0)$:

$$r_s = 0.41 + 0.0098x_1 + 0.063x_5 \qquad (4.44)$$

After that, cement content is obtained, total volume of sand and crushed stone in concrete ($V_{s+cr.s}$) are calculated:

$$V_{s+cr.s} = 1000 - \left(\frac{C}{\rho_c} + \frac{W}{\rho_w} + \frac{A}{\rho_a} \right)$$

(4.45)

where A is the fly ash content in the concrete mix, ρ_a is the density of fly ash. Contents of sand (S)and crushed stone (Cr.S) are:

$$S = V_{s+cr.s} \cdot r_s \cdot \rho_s,$$

(4.46)

$$Cr.S = V_{s+cr.s} \cdot (1-r_s) \cdot \rho_{cr.s}$$

(4.47)

where ρ_s, $\rho_{cr.s}$ are the densities of sand and crushed stone, kg/l.

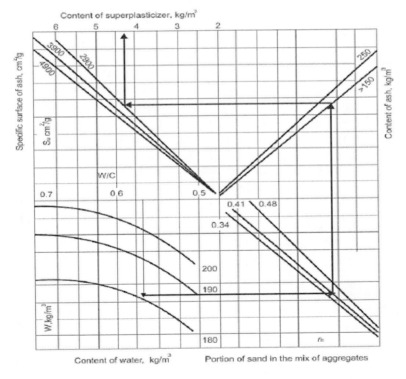

Figure 4.16. A nomogram for determining the superplasticizer's content.

For example, design a composition of ash containing self-compacting concrete with strength R_{cmp} = 20 MPa, frost resistance 200 freezing and thawing cycles and water impermeability 0.6 MPa. The concrete should be produced using Portland cement with ultimate compressive strength 40 MPa (density ρ_c=3.1 kg/l), quartz sand (ρ_s=2.65 kg/l), crushed granite fraction 5...20 mm ($\rho_{cr.s}$=2.65 kg/l), fly ash (specific surface S_a=2900 cm^2/g, ρ_a=2.52 kg/l) and superplasticizer.

Following Table 4.19, the concrete design requirements' complex provides compressive strength of 25 MPa.

The ash content is assumed to be equal to 150 kg/m^3, and the water consumption of the concrete mixture is 180 kg/m^3.

The optimal portion of sand r_s is obtained using Eq. (4.44):

$$r_s = 0.41 + 0.0098 \cdot 0 + 0.063 \cdot 0 = 0.41.$$

Following Figure 4.15, the required water-cement ratio W/C = 0.57. Content of superplasticizer obtained from Figure 4.16 is 4.46 kg/m^3. The cement content is:

$$C = 180/0.57 = 315 \text{ kg/m}$$

The total volume of sand and crushed stone is found from Eq. (4.45):

$$V_{s+cr.s} = 1000 - \left(\frac{315}{3.1} + \frac{180}{1} + \frac{150}{2.52}\right) = 658.5 \text{ kg/m}^3$$

Contents of sand and crushed stone are obtained using Eqs. (4.46) and (4.47):

$$S = 658{,}5 \cdot 0.41 \cdot 2.65 = 715 \text{ kg/m}^3$$

$$Cr.S = 658.5 \cdot (1 - 0.41) \cdot 2.65 = 1030 \text{ kg/m}^3$$

APPENDIX

Table 1. Values of Students t – criterion

Number of degrees of freedom	t-criterion at significance level α		
	0.1	0.05	0.02
1	6.31	12.7	31.82
2	2.92	4.3	6.97
3	2.35	3.18	4.54
4	2.13	2.78	3.75
5	2.01	2.57	3.37
6	1.94	2.45	3.14
7	1.89	2.36	3
8	1.86	2.31	2.9
9	1.83	2.26	2.82
10	1.81	2.23	2.76
11	1.8	2.2	2.72
12	1.78	2.18	2.68
13	1.77	2.16	2.65
14	1.76	2.14	2.62
15	1.75	2.13	2.6
16	1.75	2.12	2.58
17	1.74	2.11	2.57
18	1.73	2.1	2.55
19	1.73	2.09	2.54
20	1.73	2.09	2.53
21	1.72	2.08	2.52
22	1.72	2.07	2.51
23	1.71	2.07	2.5
24	1.71	2.06	2.49
25	1.71	2.06	2.48
26	1.71	2.05	2.47
27	1.7	20.5	2.46
28	1.7	2.05	2.46
29	1.7	2.04	2.46
30	1.68	2.02	2.42
40	1.67	2	2.39
60	1.66	1.98	2.36
120	1.64	1.96	2.33

Table 2. Dispersion ratio according to Fisher's F – criterion for α = 0.05 (confidence probability 95%)

Highest f_1	Number of degrees of freedom for dispersion Lowest f_2										
	1	2	3	4	5	6	8	10	20	50	
1	161	200	216	225	230	234	239	224	248	252	254
2	18.51	19	19.16	19.25	19.3	19.33	19.37	19.39	19.45	19.47	19.5
3	10.13	9.55	9.28	9.12	9.01	8.94	8.84	8.78	8.66	8.58	8.53
4	7.71	6.94	6.59	6.39	6.26	6.16	6.04	5.96	5.8	5.7	5.63
5	6.61	5.79	5.41	5.19	505	4.95	4.82	4.74	4.56	4.44	4.36
6	5.99	5.14	4.76	4.53	4.39	4.28	4.15	4.06	3.87	3.75	3.67
8	5.32	4.46	4.07	3.84	3.69	3.58	3.44	3.35	3.15	3.03	2.93
10	4.96	4.1	3.71	3.48	3.33	3.22	3.07	2.98	2.77	2.64	2.54
15	4.54	3.68	3.29	3.06	2.9	2.79	2.64	2.54	2.33	2.18	2.07
20	4.35	3.49	3.1	2.87	2.71	2.6	2.45	2.35	2.12	1.96	1.84
40	4.08	3.23	2.84	2.61	2.45	2.34	2.18	2.08	1.84	1.66	1.51
100	3.94	3.09	2.7	2.46	2.3	2.19	2.03	1.92	1.68	1.48	1.28
>100	3.84	2.99	2.6	2.37	2.21	2.09	1.91	1.83	1.57	1.35	1

Table 3. Rotatable Plan Matrix for $k = 4$

Plan points U	Planning matrix				Squared variables				Factors relations						Output parameter y_i
	x_1	x_2	x_3	x_4	x_1^2	x_2^2	x_3^2	x_4^2	x_1x_2	x_1x_3	x_1x_4	x_2x_3	x_2x_4	x_3x_4	
1	+1	+1	+1	+1	+1	+1	+1	+1	+1	+1	+1	+1	+1	+1	y_1
2	+1	+1	+1	-1	+1	+1	+1	+1	+1	+1	-1	+1	-1	-1	y_2
3	+1	+1	-1	+1	+1	+1	+1	+1	+1	-1	+1	-1	+1	-1	y_3
4	+1	+1	-1	-1	+1	+1	+1	+1	+1	-1	-1	-1	-1	+1	y_4
5	+1	-1	+1	+1	+1	+1	+1	+1	-1	+1	+1	-1	-1	+1	y_5
6	+1	-1	+1	-1	+1	+1	+1	+1	-1	+1	-1	-1	+1	-1	y_6
7	+1	-1	-1	+1	+1	+1	+1	+1	-1	-1	+1	+1	-1	-1	y_7
N_1 8	+1	-1	-1	-1	+1	+1	+1	+1	-1	-1	-1	+1	+1	+1	y_8
9	-1	+1	+1	+1	+1	+1	+1	+1	-1	-1	-1	+1	+1	+1	y_9
10	-1	+1	+1	-1	+1	+1	+1	+1	-1	-1	+1	+1	-1	-1	y_{10}
11	-1	+1	-1	+1	+1	+1	+1	+1	-1	+1	-1	-1	+1	-1	y_{11}
12	-1	+1	-1	-1	+1	+1	+1	+1	-1	+1	+1	-1	-1	+1	y_{12}
13	-1	-1	+1	+1	+1	+1	+1	+1	+1	-1	-1	-1	-1	+1	y_{13}
14	-1	-1	+1	-1	+1	+1	+1	+1	+1	-1	+1	-1	+1	-1	y_{14}
15	-1	-1	-1	+1	+1	+1	+1	+1	+1	+1	-1	+1	-1	-1	y_{15}
16	-1	-1	-1	-1	+1	+1	+1	+1	+1	+1	+1	+1	+1	+1	y_{16}

Table 3. (Continued)

Plan points u	Planning matrix				Squared variables				Factors relations						Output parameter y_i
	x_1	x_2	x_3	x_4	x_1^2	x_2^2	x_3^2	x_4^2	x_1x_2	x_1x_3	x_1x_4	x_2x_3	x_2x_4	x_3x_4	
17	+2	0	0	0	+4	0	0	0	0	0	0	0	0	0	y_{17}
18	-2	0	0	0	+4	0	0	0	0	0	0	0	0	0	y_{18}
19	0	+2	0	0	0	+4	0	0	0	0	0	0	0	0	y_{19}
$N\alpha20$	0	-2	0	0	0	+4	0	0	0	0	0	0	0	0	y_{20}
21	0	0	+2	0	0	0	+4	0	0	0	0	0	0	0	y_{21}
22	0	0	-2	0	0	0	+4	0	0	0	0	0	0	0	y_{22}
23	0	0	0	+2	0	0	0	+4	0	0	0	0	0	0	y_{23}
24	0	0	0	-2	0	0	0	+4	0	0	0	0	0	0	y_{24}
25	0	0	0	0	0	0	0	0	0	0	0	0	0	0	y_{25}
26	0	0	0	0	0	0	0	0	0	0	0	0	0	0	y_{26}
27	0	0	0	0	0	0	0	0	0	0	0	0	0	0	y_{27}
$n_0 28$	0	0	0	0	0	0	0	0	0	0	0	0	0	0	y_{28}
29	0	0	0	0	0	0	0	0	0	0	0	0	0	0	y_{29}
30	0	0	0	0	0	0	0	0	0	0	0	0	0	0	y_{30}
31	0	0	0	0	0	0	0	0	0	0	0	0	0	0	y_{31}

Table 4. Rotatable Plan Matrix for $k = 5$

Plan points U	Planning matrix					Squared variables					Factors relations										Output parameter y_i
	x_1	x_2	x_3	x_4	x_5	x^2_1	x^2_2	x^2_3	x^2_4	x^2_5	x_1x_2	x_1x_3	x_1x_4	x_1x_5	x_2x_3	x_2x_4	x_2x_5	x_3x_4	x_3x_5	x_4x_5	
1	+1	+1	+1	+1	+1	+1	+1	+1	+1	+1	+1	+1	+1	+1	+1	+1	+1	+1	+1	+1	y_1
2	-1	-1	+1	+1	+1	+1	+1	+1	+1	+1	+1	-1	-1	-1	-1	-1	-1	+1	+1	+1	y_2
3	-1	+1	-1	-1	-1	+1	+1	+1	+1	+1	-1	+1	+1	+1	-1	-1	-1	+1	+1	+1	y_3
4	+1	-1	-1	-1	-1	+1	+1	+1	+1	+1	-1	-1	-1	-1	+1	+1	+1	+1	+1	+1	y_4
5	-1	+1	-1	+1	+1	+1	+1	+1	+1	+1	-1	+1	-1	-1	-1	+1	+1	-1	-1	+1	y_5
6	+1	-1	-1	+1	+1	+1	+1	+1	+1	+1	-1	-1	+1	+1	+1	-1	-1	-1	-1	+1	y_6
7	+1	+1	+1	-1	-1	+1	+1	+1	+1	+1	+1	+1	-1	-1	+1	-1	-1	-1	-1	+1	y_7
8	-1	-1	+1	-1	-1	+1	+1	+1	+1	+1	+1	-1	+1	+1	-1	+1	+1	-1	-1	+1	y_8
9	-1	+1	+1	+1	-1	+1	+1	+1	+1	+1	-1	-1	-1	+1	+1	+1	-1	+1	-1	-1	y_9
10	+1	-1	+1	+1	-1	+1	+1	+1	+1	+1	-1	+1	+1	-1	-1	-1	+1	+1	-1	-1	y_{10}
11	+1	+1	-1	-1	+1	+1	+1	+1	+1	+1	+1	-1	-1	+1	-1	-1	+1	+1	-1	-1	y_{11}
12	-1	-1	-1	-1	+1	+1	+1	+1	+1	+1	+1	+1	+1	-1	+1	+1	-1	+1	-1	-1	y_{12}
13	-1	+1	+1	-1	+1	+1	+1	+1	+1	+1	-1	-1	+1	-1	+1	-1	+1	-1	+1	-1	y_{13}
14	+1	-1	+1	-1	+1	+1	+1	+1	+1	+1	-1	+1	-1	+1	-1	+1	-1	-1	+1	-1	y_{14}
15	+1	+1	-1	+1	-1	+1	+1	+1	+1	+1	+1	-1	+1	-1	-1	+1	-1	-1	+1	-1	y_{15}
16	-1	-1	-1	+1	-1	+1	+1	+1	+1	+1	+1	+1	-1	+1	+1	-1	+1	-1	+1	-1	y_{16}

N_1

Table 4. (Continued)

Plan points U	Planning matrix					Squared variables					Factors relations										Output parameter y_i
	x_1	x_2	x_3	x_4	x_5	x_1^2	x_2^2	x_3^2	x_4^2	x_5^2	x_1x_2	x_1x_3	x_1x_4	x_1x_5	x_2x_3	x_2x_4	x_2x_5	x_3x_4	x_3x_5	x_4x_5	
17	+2	0	0	0	0	+4	0	0	0	0	0	0	0	0	0	0	0	0	0	0	y_{17}
18	-2	0	0	0	0	+4	0	0	0	0	0	0	0	0	0	0	0	0	0	0	y_{18}
19	0	+2	0	0	0	0	+4	0	0	0	0	0	0	0	0	0	0	0	0	0	y_{19}
20	0	-2	0	0	0	0	+4	0	0	0	0	0	0	0	0	0	0	0	0	0	y_{20}
21	0	0	+2	0	0	0	0	+4	0	0	0	0	0	0	0	0	0	0	0	0	y_{21}
22 (N_α)	0	0	-2	0	0	0	0	+4	0	0	0	0	0	0	0	0	0	0	0	0	y_{22}
23	0	0	0	+2	0	0	0	0	+4	0	0	0	0	0	0	0	0	0	0	0	y_{23}
24	0	0	0	-2	0	0	0	0	+4	0	0	0	0	0	0	0	0	0	0	0	y_{24}
25	0	0	0	0	+2	0	0	0	0	+4	0	0	0	0	0	0	0	0	0	0	y_{25}
26	0	0	0	0	-2	0	0	0	0	+4	0	0	0	0	0	0	0	0	0	0	y_{26}
27	0	0	0	0	0	0	0	0	0	0	0	0	0	0	0	0	0	0	0	0	y_{27}
28	0	0	0	0	0	0	0	0	0	0	0	0	0	0	0	0	0	0	0	0	y_{28}
29	0	0	0	0	0	0	0	0	0	0	0	0	0	0	0	0	0	0	0	0	y_{29}
30 (n_0)	0	0	0	0	0	0	0	0	0	0	0	0	0	0	0	0	0	0	0	0	y_{30}
31	0	0	0	0	0	0	0	0	0	0	0	0	0	0	0	0	0	0	0	0	y_{31}
32	0	0	0	0	0	0	0	0	0	0	0	0	0	0	0	0	0	0	0	0	y_{32}

Table 5. Matrix of Box-Benkin plan for $k = 3$

Plan points u	Planning matrix			Squared variables			Factors relations			Output parameter y_i
	x_1	x_2	x_3	x_1^2	x_2^2	x_3^2	x_1x_2	x_1x_3	x_2x_3	
1	+1	+1	0	+1	+1	0	+1	0	0	y_1
2	+1	-1	0	+1	+1	0	-1	0	0	y_2
3	-1	+1	0	+1	+1	0	-1	0	0	y_3
4	-1	-1	0	+1	+1	0	+1	0	0	y_4
5	+1	0	+1	+1	0	+1	0	+1	0	y_5
6	+1	0	-1	+1	0	+1	0	-1	0	y_6
7	-1	0	+1	+1	0	+1	0	-1	0	y_7
8	-1	0	-1	+1	0	+1	0	+1	0	y_8
9	0	+1	+1	0	+1	+1	0	0	+1	y_9
10	0	+1	-1	0	+1	+1	0	0	-1	y_{10}
11	0	-1	+1	0	+1	+1	0	0	-1	y_{11}
12	0	-1	-1	0	+1	+1	0	0	+1	y_{12}
n_0 13	0	0	0	0	0	0	0	0	0	y_{13}
14	0	0	0	0	0	0	0	0	0	y_{14}
15	0	0	0	0	0	0	0	0	0	y_{15}

Table 6. Matrix of Box-Benkin plan for *k*=4

Plan points *u*	Planning matrix				Squared variables				Factors relations						Output parameter y_i
	x_1	x_2	x_3	x_4	x_1^2	x_2^2	x_3^2	x_4^2	x_1x_2	x_1x_3	x_1x_4	x_2x_3	x_2x_4	x_3x_4	
1	+1	+1	0	0	+1	+1	0	0	+1	0	0	0	0	0	y_1
2	+1	−1	0	0	+1	+1	0	0	−1	0	0	0	0	0	y_2
3	−1	+1	0	0	+1	+1	0	0	−1	0	0	0	0	0	y_3
4	−1	−1	0	0	+1	+1	0	0	+1	0	0	0	0	0	y_4
5	+1	0	+1	0	+1	0	+1	0	0	+1	0	0	0	0	y_5
6	+1	0	−1	0	+1	0	+1	0	0	−1	0	0	0	0	y_6
7	−1	0	+1	0	+1	0	+1	0	0	−1	0	0	0	0	y_7
8	−1	0	−1	0	+1	0	+1	0	0	+1	0	0	0	0	y_8
9	0	+1	+1	0	0	+1	+1	0	0	0	0	+1	0	0	y_9
10	0	+1	−1	0	0	+1	+1	0	0	0	0	−1	0	0	y_{10}
11	0	−1	+1	0	0	+1	+1	0	0	0	0	−1	0	0	y_{11}
12	0	−1	−1	0	0	+1	+1	0	0	0	0	+1	0	0	y_{12}
13	0	0	+1	+1	0	0	+1	+1	0	0	0	0	0	+1	y_{13}
14	0	0	−1	+1	0	0	+1	+1	0	0	0	0	0	−1	y_{14}
15	0	0	+1	−1	0	0	+1	+1	0	0	0	0	0	−1	y_{15}
16	0	0	−1	−1	0	0	+1	+1	0	0	0	0	0	+1	y_{16}
17	+1	0	0	+1	+1	0	0	+1	0	0	+1	0	0	0	y_{17}
18	+1	0	0	−1	+1	0	0	+1	0	0	−1	0	0	0	y_{18}
19	−1	0	0	+1	+1	0	0	+1	0	0	−1	0	0	0	y_{19}
20	−1	0	0	−1	+1	0	0	+1	0	0	+1	0	0	0	y_{20}
21	0	+1	0	+1	0	+1	0	+1	0	0	0	0	+1	0	y_{21}
22	0	+1	0	−1	0	+1	0	+1	0	0	0	0	−1	0	y_{22}
23	0	−1	0	+1	0	+1	0	+1	0	0	0	0	−1	0	y_{23}
24	0	−1	0	−1	0	+1	0	+1	0	0	0	0	+1	0	y_{24}
25	0	0	0	0	0	0	0	0	0	0	0	0	0	0	y_{25}
n_0 26	0	0	0	0	0	0	0	0	0	0	0	0	0	0	y_{26}
27	0	0	0	0	0	0	0	0	0	0	0	0	0	0	y_{27}

Table 7. Matrix of Box-Benkin plan for $k=5$

Plan points U	Planning matrix					Squared variables					Factors relations											Output parameter y_i
	x_1	x_2	x_3	x_4	x_5	x_1^2	x_2^2	x_3^2	x_4^2	x_5^2	x_1x_2	x_1x_3	x_1x_4	x_1x_5	x_2x_3	x_2x_4	x_2x_5	x_3x_4	x_3x_5	x_4x_5	y_i
1	+1	+1	0	0	0	+1	+1	0	0	0	+1	0	0	0	0	0	0	0	0	0	y_1
2	+1	-1	0	0	0	+1	+1	0	0	0	-1	0	0	0	0	0	0	0	0	0	y_2
3	-1	+1	0	0	0	+1	+1	0	0	0	-1	0	0	0	0	0	0	0	0	0	y_3
4	-1	-1	0	0	0	+1	+1	0	0	0	+1	0	0	0	0	0	0	0	0	0	y_4
5	+1	0	+1	0	0	+1	0	+1	0	0	0	+1	0	0	0	0	0	0	0	0	y_5
6	+1	0	-1	0	0	+1	0	+1	0	0	0	-1	0	0	0	0	0	0	0	0	y_6
7	-1	0	+1	0	0	+1	0	+1	0	0	0	-1	0	0	0	0	0	0	0	0	y_7
8	-1	0	-1	0	0	+1	0	+1	0	0	0	+1	0	0	0	0	0	0	0	0	y_8
9	0	+1	+1	0	0	0	+1	+1	0	0	0	0	0	0	+1	0	0	0	0	0	y_9
10	0	+1	-1	0	0	0	+1	+1	0	0	0	0	0	0	-1	0	0	0	0	0	y_{10}
11	0	-1	+1	0	0	0	+1	+1	0	0	0	0	0	0	-1	0	0	0	0	0	y_{11}
12	0	-1	-1	0	0	0	+1	+1	0	0	0	0	0	0	+1	0	0	0	0	0	y_{12}
13	0	0	+1	+1	0	0	0	+1	+1	0	0	0	0	0	0	0	0	+1	0	0	y_{13}
14	0	0	+1	-1	0	0	0	+1	+1	0	0	0	0	0	0	0	0	-1	0	0	y_{14}
15	0	0	-1	+1	0	0	0	+1	+1	0	0	0	0	0	0	0	0	-1	0	0	y_{15}

Table 7. (Continued)

Plan points U	Planning matrix					Squared variables					Factors relations										Output parameter y_i
	x_1	x_2	x_3	x_4	x_5	x_1^2	x_2^2	x_3^2	x_4^2	x_5^2	x_1x_2	x_1x_3	x_1x_4	x_1x_5	x_2x_3	x_2x_4	x_2x_5	x_3x_4	x_3x_5	x_4x_5	
16	0	0	−1	−1	0	0	0	+1	+1	0	0	0	0	0	0	0	0	+1	0	0	y_{16}
17	+1	0	0	+1	0	+1	0	0	+1	0	0	0	+1	0	0	0	0	0	0	0	y_{17}
18	+1	0	0	−1	0	+1	0	0	+1	0	0	0	−1	0	0	0	0	0	0	0	y_{18}
19	−1	0	0	+1	0	+1	0	0	+1	0	0	0	−1	0	0	0	0	0	0	0	y_{19}
20	−1	0	0	−1	0	+1	0	0	+1	0	0	0	+1	0	0	0	0	0	0	0	y_{20}
21	0	+1	0	+1	0	0	+1	0	+1	0	0	0	0	0	0	+1	0	0	0	0	y_{21}
22	0	+1	0	−1	0	0	+1	0	+1	0	0	0	0	0	0	−1	0	0	0	0	y_{22}
23	0	−1	0	+1	0	0	+1	0	+1	0	0	0	0	0	0	−1	0	0	0	0	y_{23}
24	0	−1	0	−1	0	0	+1	0	+1	0	0	0	0	0	0	+1	0	0	0	0	y_{24}
25	0	+1	0	0	+1	0	+1	0	0	+1	0	0	0	0	0	0	+1	0	0	0	y_{25}
26	0	+1	0	0	−1	0	+1	0	0	+1	0	0	0	0	0	0	−1	0	0	0	y_{26}
27	0	−1	0	0	+1	0	+1	0	0	+1	0	0	0	0	0	0	−1	0	0	0	y_{27}
28	0	−1	0	0	−1	0	+1	0	0	+1	0	0	0	0	0	0	+1	0	0	0	y_{28}
29	0	0	0	+1	+1	0	0	0	+1	+1	0	0	0	0	0	0	0	0	0	+1	y_{29}
30	0	0	0	+1	−1	0	0	0	+1	+1	0	0	0	0	0	0	0	0	0	−1	y_{30}
31	0	0	0	−1	+1	0	0	0	+1	+1	0	0	0	0	0	0	0	0	0	−1	y_{31}
32	0	0	0	−1	−1	0	0	0	+1	+1	0	0	0	0	0	0	0	0	0	+1	y_{32}
33	0	0	+1	0	+1	0	0	+1	+1	+1	0	0	0	0	0	0	0	0	+1	0	y_{33}
34	0	0	+1	0	−1	0	0	+1	+1	+1	0	0	0	0	0	0	0	0	−1	0	y_{34}
35	0	0	−1	0	+1	0	0	+1	+1	+1	0	0	0	0	0	0	0	0	−1	0	y_{35}

Plan points U	Planning matrix					Squared variables					Factors relations										Output parameter y_i
	x_1	x_2	x_3	x_4	x_5	x_1^2	x_2^2	x_3^2	x_4^2	x_5^2	x_1x_2	x_1x_3	x_1x_4	x_1x_5	x_2x_3	x_2x_4	x_2x_5	x_3x_4	x_3x_5	x_4x_5	
36	0	0	-1	0	-1	0	0	+1	+1	+1	0	0	0	0	0	0	0	0	+1	0	y_{36}
37	+1	0	0	0	+1	+1	0	0	+1	+1	0	0	0	+1	0	0	0	0	0	0	y_{37}
38	+1	0	0	0	-1	+1	0	0	+1	+1	0	0	0	-1	0	0	0	0	0	0	y_{38}
39	-1	0	0	0	+1	+1	0	0	+1	+1	0	0	0	-1	0	0	0	0	0	0	y_{39}
40	-1	0	0	0	-1	+1	0	0	+1	+1	0	0	0	+1	0	0	0	0	0	0	y_{40}
41	0	0	0	0	0	0	0	0	0	0	0	0	0	0	0	0	0	0	0	0	y_{41}
42	0	0	0	0	0	0	0	0	0	0	0	0	0	0	0	0	0	0	0	0	y_{42}
43	0	0	0	0	0	0	0	0	0	0	0	0	0	0	0	0	0	0	0	0	y_{43}
44	0	0	0	0	0	0	0	0	0	0	0	0	0	0	0	0	0	0	0	0	y_{44}
45	0	0	0	0	0	0	0	0	0	0	0	0	0	0	0	0	0	0	0	0	y_{45}
46	0	0	0	0	0	0	0	0	0	0	0	0	0	0	0	0	0	0	0	0	y_{46}

Table 8. Plan matrix B_4 for k = 4

Plan points U	x_1	x_2	x_3	x_4	x^2_1	x^2_2	x^2_3	x^2_4	$x_1 x_2$	$x_1 x_3$	$x_1 x_4$	$x_2 x_3$	$x_2 x_4$	$x_3 x_4$	Output parameter y_i
1	+1	+1	+1	+1	+1	+1	+1	+1	+1	+1	+1	+1	+1	+1	y_1
2	+1	+1	+1	-1	+1	+1	+1	+1	+1	+1	-1	+1	-1	-1	y_2
3	+1	+1	-1	+1	+1	+1	+1	+1	+1	-1	+1	-1	+1	-1	y_3
4	+1	+1	-1	-1	+1	+1	+1	+1	+1	-1	-1	-1	-1	+1	y_4
5	+1	-1	+1	+1	+1	+1	+1	+1	-1	+1	+1	-1	-1	+1	y_5
6	+1	-1	+1	-1	+1	+1	+1	+1	-1	+1	-1	-1	+1	-1	y_6
7	+1	-1	-1	+1	+1	+1	+1	+1	-1	-1	+1	+1	-1	-1	y_7
8	+1	-1	-1	-1	+1	+1	+1	+1	-1	-1	-1	+1	+1	+1	y_8
9	-1	+1	+1	+1	+1	+1	+1	+1	-1	-1	-1	+1	+1	+1	y_9
10	-1	+1	+1	-1	+1	+1	+1	+1	-1	-1	+1	+1	-1	-1	y_{10}
11	-1	+1	-1	+1	+1	+1	+1	+1	-1	+1	-1	-1	+1	-1	y_{11}
12	-1	+1	-1	-1	+1	+1	+1	+1	-1	+1	+1	-1	-1	+1	y_{12}
13	-1	-1	+1	+1	+1	+1	+1	+1	+1	-1	-1	-1	-1	+1	y_{13}
14	-1	-1	+1	-1	+1	+1	+1	+1	+1	-1	+1	-1	+1	-1	y_{14}
15	-1	-1	-1	+1	+1	+1	+1	+1	+1	+1	-1	+1	-1	-1	y_{15}
16	-1	-1	-1	-1	+1	+1	+1	+1	+1	+1	+1	+1	+1	+1	y_{16}

N_1

Plan points U		Planning matrix				Squared variables				Factors relations						Output parameter y_i
		x_1	x_2	x_3	x_4	x_1^2	x_2^2	x_3^2	x_4^2	$x_1 x_2$	$x_1 x_3$	$x_1 x_4$	$x_2 x_3$	$x_2 x_4$	$x_3 x_4$	
$N\alpha$	17	+1	0	0	0	+1	0	0	0	0	0	0	0	0	0	y_{17}
	18	-1	0	0	0	+1	0	0	0	0	0	0	0	0	0	y_{18}
	19	0	+1	0	0	0	+1	0	0	0	0	0	0	0	0	y_{19}
	20	0	-1	0	0	0	+1	0	0	0	0	0	0	0	0	y_{20}
	21	0	0	+1	0	0	0	+1	0	0	0	0	0	0	0	y_{21}
	22	0	0	-1	0	0	0	+1	0	0	0	0	0	0	0	y_{22}
	23	0	0	0	+1	0	0	0	+1	0	0	0	0	0	0	y_{23}
	24	0	0	0	-1	0	0	0	+1	0	0	0	0	0	0	y_{24}

Table 9. Plan matrix B_4 for $k = 5$

Plan points U	Planning matrix					Squared variables					Factors relations										Output parameter y_i
	x_1	x_2	x_3	x_4	x_5	x_1^2	x_2^2	x_3^2	x_4^2	x_5^2	x_1x_2	x_1x_3	x_1x_4	x_1x_5	x_2x_3	x_2x_4	x_2x_5	x_3x_4	x_3x_5	x_4x_5	
1	+1	+1	+1	+1	+1	+1	+1	+1	+1	+1	+1	+1	+1	+1	+1	+1	+1	+1	+1	+1	y_1
2	+1	+1	+1	+1	−1	+1	+1	+1	+1	+1	+1	+1	+1	−1	+1	+1	−1	+1	−1	−1	y_2
3	+1	+1	+1	−1	+1	+1	+1	+1	+1	+1	+1	+1	−1	+1	+1	−1	+1	−1	+1	−1	y_3
4	+1	+1	+1	−1	−1	+1	+1	+1	+1	+1	+1	+1	−1	−1	+1	−1	−1	−1	−1	+1	y_4
5	+1	+1	−1	+1	+1	+1	+1	+1	+1	+1	+1	−1	+1	+1	−1	+1	+1	−1	−1	+1	y_5
6	+1	+1	−1	+1	−1	+1	+1	+1	+1	+1	+1	−1	+1	−1	−1	+1	−1	−1	+1	−1	y_6
7	+1	+1	−1	−1	+1	+1	+1	+1	+1	+1	+1	−1	−1	+1	−1	−1	+1	+1	−1	−1	y_7
8	+1	+1	−1	−1	−1	+1	+1	+1	+1	+1	+1	−1	−1	−1	−1	−1	−1	+1	+1	+1	y_8
9	+1	−1	+1	+1	+1	+1	+1	+1	+1	+1	−1	+1	+1	+1	−1	−1	−1	+1	+1	+1	y_9
10	+1	−1	+1	+1	−1	+1	+1	+1	+1	+1	−1	+1	+1	−1	−1	−1	+1	+1	−1	−1	y_{10}
11	+1	−1	+1	−1	+1	+1	+1	+1	+1	+1	−1	+1	−1	+1	−1	+1	−1	−1	+1	−1	y_{11}
12	+1	−1	+1	−1	−1	+1	+1	+1	+1	+1	−1	+1	−1	−1	−1	+1	+1	−1	−1	+1	y_{12}
13	+1	−1	−1	+1	+1	+1	+1	+1	+1	+1	−1	−1	+1	+1	+1	−1	−1	−1	−1	+1	y_{13}
14	+1	−1	−1	+1	−1	+1	+1	+1	+1	+1	−1	−1	+1	−1	+1	−1	+1	−1	+1	−1	y_{14}
15	+1	−1	−1	−1	+1	+1	+1	+1	+1	+1	−1	−1	−1	+1	+1	+1	−1	+1	−1	−1	y_{15}
16	+1	+1	−1	−1	−1	+1	+1	+1	+1	+1	−1	−1	−1	−1	+1	+1	+1	+1	+1	+1	y_{16}
17	−1	+1	+1	+1	+1	+1	+1	+1	+1	+1	−1	−1	−1	−1	+1	+1	+1	+1	+1	+1	y_{17}

Plan points U	Planning matrix					Squared variables					Factors relations										Output parameter y_i
	x_1	x_2	x_3	x_4	x_5	x^2_1	x^2_2	x^2_3	x^2_4	x^2_5	x_1x_2	x_1x_3	x_1x_4	x_1x_5	x_2x_3	x_2x_4	x_2x_5	x_3x_4	x_3x_5	x_4x_5	
18	-1	+1	+1	+1	-1	+1	+1	+1	+1	+1	-1	-1	-1	+1	+1	+1	-1	+1	-1	-1	y_{18}
19	-1	+1	+1	-1	+1	+1	+1	+1	+1	+1	-1	-1	+1	-1	+1	-1	+1	-1	+1	-1	y_{19}
20	-1	+1	+1	-1	-1	+1	+1	+1	+1	+1	-1	-1	+1	+1	+1	-1	-1	-1	-1	+1	y_{20}
21	-1	+1	-1	+1	+1	+1	+1	+1	+1	+1	-1	+1	-1	-1	-1	+1	+1	-1	-1	+1	y_{21}
22	-1	+1	-1	+1	-1	+1	+1	+1	+1	+1	-1	+1	-1	+1	-1	+1	-1	-1	+1	-1	y_{22}
23	-1	+1	-1	-1	+1	+1	+1	+1	+1	+1	-1	+1	+1	-1	-1	-1	+1	+1	-1	-1	y_{23}
24	-1	+1	-1	-1	-1	+1	+1	+1	+1	+1	-1	+1	+1	+1	-1	-1	-1	+1	+1	+1	y_{24}
25	-1	-1	+1	+1	+1	+1	+1	+1	+1	+1	+1	-1	-1	-1	-1	-1	-1	+1	+1	+1	y_{25}
26	-1	-1	+1	+1	-1	+1	+1	+1	+1	+1	+1	-1	-1	+1	-1	-1	+1	+1	-1	-1	y_{26}
27	-1	-1	+1	-1	+1	+1	+1	+1	+1	+1	+1	-1	+1	-1	-1	+1	-1	-1	+1	-1	y_{27}
28	-1	-1	+1	-1	-1	+1	+1	+1	+1	+1	+1	-1	+1	+1	-1	+1	+1	-1	-1	+1	y_{28}
29	-1	-1	-1	+1	+1	+1	+1	+1	+1	+1	+1	+1	-1	-1	+1	-1	-1	-1	-1	+1	y_{29}
30	-1	-1	-1	+1	-1	+1	+1	+1	+1	+1	+1	+1	-1	+1	+1	-1	+1	-1	+1	-1	y_{30}
31	-1	-1	-1	-1	+1	+1	+1	+1	+1	+1	+1	+1	+1	-1	+1	+1	-1	+1	-1	-1	y_{31}

Table 9. (Continued)

Plan points U	x_1	x_2	x_3	x_4	x_5	x_1^2	x_2^2	x_3^2	x_4^2	x_5^2	x_1x_2	x_1x_3	x_1x_4	x_1x_5	x_2x_3	x_2x_4	x_2x_5	x_3x_4	x_3x_5	x_4x_5	Output parameter y_i
32	-1	-1	-1	-1	-1	+1	+1	+1	+1	+1	+1	+1	+1	+1	+1	+1	+1	+1	+1	+1	y_{32}
33	+1	0	0	0	0	+1	0	0	0	0	0	0	0	0	0	0	0	0	0	0	y_{33}
34	-1	0	0	0	0	+1	0	0	0	0	0	0	0	0	0	0	0	0	0	0	y_{34}
35	0	+1	0	0	0	0	+1	0	0	0	0	0	0	0	0	0	0	0	0	0	y_{35}
36	0	-1	0	0	0	0	+1	0	0	0	0	0	0	0	0	0	0	0	0	0	y_{36}
37	0	0	+1	0	0	0	0	+1	0	0	0	0	0	0	0	0	0	0	0	0	y_{37}
38	0	0	-1	0	0	0	0	+1	0	0	0	0	0	0	0	0	0	0	0	0	y_{38}
39	0	0	0	+1	0	0	0	0	+1	0	0	0	0	0	0	0	0	0	0	0	y_{39}
40	0	0	0	-1	0	0	0	0	+1	0	0	0	0	0	0	0	0	0	0	0	y_{40}
41	0	0	0	0	+1	0	0	0	0	+1	0	0	0	0	0	0	0	0	0	0	y_{41}
42	0	0	0	0	-1	0	0	0	0	+1	0	0	0	0	0	0	0	0	0	0	y_{42}

$N\alpha$

Table 10. Matrix of Ha₅ plan, close to D – optimal for $k = 5$

Plan points U	Planning matrix					Squared variables					Factors relations										Output parameter y_i
	x_1	x_2	x_3	x_4	x_5	x_1^2	x_2^2	x_3^2	x_4^2	x_5^2	x_1x_2	x_1x_3	x_1x_4	x_1x_5	x_2x_3	x_2x_4	x_2x_5	x_3x_4	x_3x_5	x_4x_5	
1	+	+	+	+	+	+	+	+	+	+	+	+	+	+	+	+	+	+	+	+	y_1
2	−	−	+	+	+	+	+	+	+	+	+	−	−	−	−	−	−	+	+	+	y_2
3	−	+	−	−	−	+	+	+	+	+	−	+	+	+	−	−	−	+	+	+	y_3
4	+	−	−	−	−	+	+	+	+	+	−	−	−	−	+	+	+	+	+	+	y_4
5	−	+	−	+	+	+	+	+	+	+	−	+	−	−	−	+	+	−	−	+	y_5
6	+	−	+	−	+	+	+	+	+	+	−	+	−	+	−	−	+	−	−	+	y_6
7	+	−	+	−	−	+	+	+	+	+	−	+	−	−	−	−	+	−	−	+	y_7
8	−	+	+	−	−	+	+	+	+	+	−	−	+	+	+	−	−	−	−	+	y_8
9	−	−	−	+	−	+	+	+	+	+	+	+	−	+	+	−	+	−	−	−	y_9
10	+	+	−	−	+	+	+	+	+	+	+	−	−	+	−	−	+	+	−	−	y_{10}
11	+	−	+	−	+	+	+	+	+	+	−	+	−	+	−	+	−	+	+	−	y_{11}
12	−	−	+	−	+	+	+	+	+	+	+	−	+	−	−	+	−	+	+	−	y_{12}
13	−	−	−	−	+	+	+	+	+	+	+	+	+	−	+	+	−	−	+	−	y_{13}
14	+	−	+	−	−	+	+	+	+	+	−	+	+	−	+	+	+	−	+	−	y_{14}
15	+	+	−	+	−	+	+	+	+	+	+	−	+	+	−	+	+	−	+	−	y_{15}
16	−	−	−	+	−	+	+	+	+	+	+	+	−	+	+	−	+	−	+	−	y_{16}

N_1

Table 10. (Continued)

Plan points U / N_λ	Planning matrix					Squared variables					Factors relations										Output parameter y_i
	x_1	x_2	x_3	x_4	x_5	x_1^2	x_2^2	x_3^2	x_4^2	x_5^2	x_1x_2	x_1x_3	x_1x_4	x_1x_5	x_2x_3	x_2x_4	x_2x_5	x_3x_4	x_3x_5	x_4x_5	
17	+1	0	0	0	0	+1	0	0	0	0	0	0	0	0	0	0	0	0	0	0	y_{17}
18	-1	0	0	0	0	+1	0	0	0	0	0	0	0	0	0	0	0	0	0	0	y_{18}
19	0	+1	0	0	0	0	+1	0	0	0	0	0	0	0	0	0	0	0	0	0	y_{19}
20	0	-1	0	0	0	0	+1	0	0	0	0	0	0	0	0	0	0	0	0	0	y_{20}
21	0	0	+1	0	0	0	0	+1	0	0	0	0	0	0	0	0	0	0	0	0	y_{21}
22	0	0	-1	0	0	0	0	+1	0	0	0	0	0	0	0	0	0	0	0	0	y_{22}
23	0	0	0	+1	0	0	0	0	+1	0	0	0	0	0	0	0	0	0	0	0	y_{23}
24	0	0	0	-1	0	0	0	0	+1	0	0	0	0	0	0	0	0	0	0	0	y_{24}
25	0	0	0	0	+1	0	0	0	0	+1	0	0	0	0	0	0	0	0	0	0	y_{25}
26	0	0	0	0	-1	0	0	0	0	+1	0	0	0	0	0	0	0	0	0	0	y_{26}
n_0 27	0	0	0	0	0	0	0	0	0	0	0	0	0	0	0	0	0	0	0	0	y_{27}

Table 11. Simplex-grided plans for building three-component "content – property" models"

Experiment No.	Model													y
	First order			Second order			Incomplete third order			Third order			
	v_1	v_2	v_3	v_1	v_2	v_3	v_1	v_2	v_3	v_1	v_2	v_3	
1	1	0	0	1	0	0	1	0	0	1	0	0	y_1
2	0	1	0	0	1	0	0	1	0	0	1	0	y_2
3	0	0	1	0	0	1	0	0	1	0	0	1	y_3
4				1/2	1/2	0	1/2	1/2	0	–	–	–	y_{12}
5				1/2	0	1/2	1/2	0	1/2	–	–	–	y_{13}
6				0	1/2	1/2	0	1/2	1/2	–	–	–	y_{23}
7							1/3	1/3	1/3	1/3	1/3	1/3	y_{123}
8										1/3	2/3	0	y_{122}
9										2/3	1/3	0	y_{112}
10										1/3	0	2/3	y_{133}
11										2/3	0	1/3	y_{113}
12										0	1/3	2/3	y_{233}
13										0	2/3	1/3	y_{223}

REFERENCES

Ahnazarova S.L., Kafarov V.V. *Methods of Optimization of Experiment* in *Chemical Technology*. Vushay Shkola, Moscow, Russia.

Barker, Thomas. B. *Quality by Experimental Design*. Marcel Dekker Inc., New York, NY, USA, 1985.

Box, G. E. P., W. G. Hunter, and J. S. Hunter. *Statistics for Experimenters: An Introduction to Design, Data Analysis, and Model Building*. John Wiley and Sons, New York, NY, USA, 1978.

Cochran, W. G. and Cox, G. M. *Experimental Designs*. John Wiley and Sons, New York, NY, USA, 1950

Del Vecchio, R.J. *Understanding Design of Experiments*. Hanser Publishers, Munich, 1997.

Hicks, C. R. *Fundamental Concepts in the Design of Experiments*, Holt, Rinehart and Winston, New York, NY, USA, 1994.

Montgomery, Douglas C. *Design and Analysis of Experiments*. John Wiley and Sons, New York, NY, USA, 1991.

Pazman, A. *Foundations of Optimum Experimental Design*. D. Reidel Publishing Company, Dordrect, Holland, 1986.

Plackett R.L. *Regression Analysis*, Clarendon Press, Oxford, 1960.

Pukelsheim, F. *Optimal Design of Experiments*. John Wiley and Sons, New York, NY, USA,1993

Voznesenski V.A., Layshenko T.V., Ogarkov B.L. *Numeral Methods of Decision of Construction-Technological Tasks on Computer*. Vusha Shkola, Kiev, Ukraine, 1989.

Dvorkin L.I. *Optimal concrete compositions design*, Vusha Shkola, Lviv, Ukraine, 1981.

Dvorkin L. I. Dvorkin O.L. *Basics of concrete science*. Stroybeton, S-Peterburg, 2006.

INDEX

A

abstraction, 6
accelerator, 27
adaptation, 10
additives, 50, 97, 106, 107
adhesive properties, 100
adjustment, 10, 11, 109
age, 36, 70, 133, 135
algorithm, 11, 104, 136
amplitude, 68
arithmetic, 32
assessment, 13, 21, 28, 32, 91
automation, 3

B

bias, 67

C

calcium, 27
capillary, 9, 94, 95
casting, 4
causal relationship, 6
chemical, ix, 4, 8, 12, 99, 101
Chicago, 87
complex interactions, 101
complexity, 1, 4, 11, 88

composition, 1, 4, 6, 8, 9, 12, 15, 17, 18, 27,
    60, 63, 64, 65, 67, 68, 69, 70, 76, 84, 87,
    88, 89, 90, 91, 92, 95, 96, 98, 99, 100,
    101, 102, 103, 104, 105, 106, 107, 108,
    109, 112, 117, 122, 127, 130, 136, 143,
    146
compression, 89, 92, 93, 97
computer, 7, 8
computerization, 88
computing, 3
construction, 4, 14, 87, 89, 90, 92
consumers, 14
consumption, 12, 50, 91, 98, 99, 101, 102,
    103, 104, 108, 113, 114, 115, 116, 117,
    120, 122, 123, 125, 126, 127, 129, 130,
    131, 133, 143, 146
cooling, 101
coordination, 21
correlation, 18, 20, 25
corrosion, 92, 98, 99
cost, 11, 12, 13, 14, 17, 18, 19, 83, 87, 89,
    90, 98, 102
creep, 89, 93, 94, 95, 96
cycles, 18, 96, 108, 130, 131, 133, 135, 137,
    138, 139, 140, 143, 144, 146

D

data processing, 6, 112
decision-making process, 31

deformation, 4, 8, 11, 84
dependent variable, 64, 106
derivatives, 82
designers, 90
destruction, 8, 11
destructive process, 100, 101
deviation, 38, 57
dispersion, 32, 34, 35, 38, 39, 40, 41, 45, 46, 51, 52, 55, 57, 59, 66, 99, 103, 148
distribution, 21, 27
drawing, 83, 101
dry matter, 27
durability, 1

E

efficiency criteria, 4
electricity, 18
emission, 93
energy, 9, 18, 98
energy consumption, 98
engineering, 32, 92, 108
environment, 4, 5, 11, 93
evolution, 98
exaggeration, 88
exclusion, 20, 84
expenditures, 112, 121, 123
exposure, 23, 26, 100, 101
external environment, 11
extremum problems, 84

F

fluctuations, 27
forecasting, 88
formaldehyde, 117, 122
formation, 9, 88, 98, 101
formula, 32, 33, 35, 67, 77, 94, 96, 117
freedom, 32, 34, 35, 36, 147, 148
freezing, 18, 96, 133, 137, 146
frost, 1, 9, 18, 22, 89, 91, 93, 94, 95, 96, 97, 99, 100, 102, 105, 108, 128, 130, 131, 133, 134, 136, 137, 138, 142, 143, 146
frost resistance, 1, 9, 18, 22, 89, 91, 93, 94, 95, 96, 97, 99, 100, 102, 105, 108, 128, 130, 131, 133, 134, 136, 137, 138, 142, 143, 146
full factorial experiment (FFE), 27
functional approach, 5

G

geometry, 84
glue, 88
growth, 85
guidelines, 84

H

hardening conditions, 13
hardening process, 4, 98
heating rate, 101
history, 8
homogeneity, 103
humidity, 27, 93, 128, 129, 143
Hunter, 167
hypothesis, 16, 21, 27, 32

I

identification, 109
image, 83
independent variable, 15, 16
isothermal heating, 21, 26, 101, 115
Israel, ix

J

justification, 87

L

Lagrange multipliers, 85
lead, 3
lifetime, 12, 13
light, 96, 105
linear dependence, 25
linear programming, 102, 107

M

management, 3, 5, 9, 11
manpower, 90
manufacturing, ix, 3, 8, 87
mass, 27, 54, 68, 79, 85
materials, 4, 7, 9, 13, 25, 36, 65, 68, 87, 88, 93, 97, 101, 102, 109, 111, 122, 127, 128
mathematical methods, 1, 3, 5, 7, 10
mathematical planning of experiments (MPE), ix
matrix, 21, 25, 27, 28, 29, 30, 31, 32, 33, 34, 35, 37, 39, 40, 42, 45, 46, 47, 48, 49, 51, 52, 55, 58, 71, 72, 74, 89, 104, 149, 150, 151, 152, 153, 154, 155, 156, 157, 158, 159, 160, 161, 162, 163, 164
matter, 27
measurement, 8
mechanical properties, 4, 8
meter, 90, 163
methodological principles, ix
methodology, ix, 2, 3, 78, 87, 88
models, vii, ix, 1, 2, 4, 5, 6, 7, 8, 9, 10, 11, 31, 44, 68, 75, 77, 78, 85, 102, 103, 105, 106, 107, 108, 109, 111, 112, 116, 117, 123, 124, 126, 129, 130, 131, 136, 142, 143, 165
modulus, 23, 26, 36, 111, 128, 133, 136, 142
moisture, 21
Moscow, 167
multidimensional, 77
multiple-factor dependencies, ix

N

National University of Water Management and Nature Resources Use, ix
nitrite, 27

O

opportunities, 25, 88, 99

optimization, 1, 2, 5, 6, 7, 10, 12, 15, 16, 17, 18, 19, 20, 46, 84, 85, 87, 90, 96, 98, 100, 102, 103, 104, 105, 107, 111, 112, 130
optimization method, 7
orthogonality, 46

P

permeability, 9
physical and mechanical properties, 4
physics, 8
polymer, 70, 73
porosity, 8, 94, 95
porous space, 9, 89
principles, ix, 1, 5, 8, 9, 105
probability, 1, 21, 35, 36, 42, 51, 60, 112, 148
process duration, 101, 136
production technology, 11, 21
programming, 92, 102, 107

Q

quartz, 21, 36, 42, 96, 111, 117, 122, 127, 128, 133, 136, 146
questioning, 21
questionnaire, 21, 23

R

radius, 46, 50
recommendations, 4
regression, 2, 5, 10, 11, 16, 27, 28, 31, 32, 34, 35, 37, 38, 40, 41, 42, 44, 45, 46, 47, 50, 51, 52, 53, 56, 57, 58, 59, 60, 69, 71, 76, 78, 79, 80, 81, 82, 83, 103, 106
regression analysis, 10, 11, 31, 32
regression equation, 2, 5, 16, 27, 28, 34, 35, 37, 38, 40, 41, 42, 46, 47, 50, 51, 52, 53, 56, 58, 60, 69, 71, 76, 78, 79, 80, 81, 82, 83, 103, 106
reinforcement, 14, 98
relevance, 32

reliability, 5, 87
requirements, 3, 11, 13, 15, 87, 88, 97, 135, 139, 146
researchers, 9, 20, 21, 100
reserves, 3
resistance, 1, 9, 18, 22, 89, 91, 93, 94, 95, 96, 97, 98, 99, 100, 102, 105, 108, 128, 130, 131, 133, 135, 136, 137, 138, 139, 140, 142, 143, 144, 146
resources, 7, 12, 14, 18, 19, 78, 83, 87, 88
response, 5, 15, 44, 70, 73, 78, 80, 83, 84, 85, 98, 103, 104, 105, 109
restrictions, 91, 98
rheology, 8
risk, 32
root, 106
rules, 1, 96, 97
Russia, 102, 167

S

SAS, 99, 100
science, ix, 4, 5, 9, 10, 12, 88, 89, 167
shape, 64, 100
significance level, 31, 34, 35, 39, 147
slag, 70, 73, 76, 108, 123, 124, 126, 127, 128
software, 7
solid phase, 89
solution, 7, 8, 12, 13, 87, 89, 102, 104, 105, 112, 117, 124, 130, 143
specialists, vii
specific surface, 146
standard deviation, 38
state, 6, 8, 64
statistical processing, 111
statistics, 28
storage, 21
structural characteristics, 9
structure, 4, 8, 9, 11, 18, 26, 84, 89, 90, 96, 98, 99, 100
structure formation, 9
subgroups, 92, 95
substitution, 81
synthesis, 9

system analysis, 1, 3, 4, 12, 88

T

task conditions, 92
techniques, 25, 92, 98
technological revolution, 3
technologies, 87
technology, vii, ix, 1, 2, 3, 4, 5, 6, 7, 8, 9, 10, 11, 12, 16, 21, 35, 45, 68, 70, 71, 73, 74, 84, 87, 88, 90, 91, 99, 102
temperature, 21, 23, 27, 42, 99, 101, 122, 128
tensile strength, 89
testing, 6, 21
three-dimensional space, 64, 83
total costs, 12
transformation, 103, 106
transformations, 81, 84
transportation, 12, 90
treatment, 13, 21, 99, 100, 101, 103, 115, 116, 119, 122, 123, 124, 125, 126, 127, 128, 129, 131, 136, 137, 138, 143

U

Ukraine, ix, 167
uniform, 21, 27, 64, 91, 103
USA, 167

V

variable factor, 5, 78
variables, 7, 8, 15, 16, 28, 40, 42, 64, 106, 149, 150, 151, 152, 153, 154, 155, 156, 157, 158, 159, 160, 161, 162, 163, 164
velocity, 21, 23, 24, 26

W

water absorption, 94, 100
water-cement ratio (W/C), 17, 21, 91
wear, 89
workers, vii

Y

yield, 9, 13, 18, 28, 92